METALWORK AND MACHINING
HINTS AND TIPS

Metalwork and Machining Hints and Tips

Ian Bradley

ARGUS BOOKS

Argus Books Limited
Wolsey House
Wolsey Road
Hemel Hempstead
Hertfordshire HP2 4SS
England

First published by Argus Books 1988
© Ian Bradley 1988

ISBN 0 85242 947 9

Phototypesetting by Goodfellow & Egan, Cambridge.
Printed and bound by LR Printing Services Ltd, Manor Royal, Crawley, West Sussex, RH10 2QN, England.

CONTENTS

PREFACE

Correspondents have suggested to the author that much of the information put out by him over many years should be collected, edited and published as additional volumes to 'The Amateur's Workshop'.

Accordingly, this material has been sifted and a choice made of subjects that should be of value both to the experienced amateur as well as to the novice himself.

Some of these subjects are basic to workshop practice, others are of a more advanced nature, but as none of them appear to be covered collectively in other publications, it is hoped that many workers will find this compilation useful.

Hungerford, 1988   Ian Bradley

CHAPTER 1

ARBORS AND MANDRELS

One of the minor problems of lathe work is to re-chuck partly machined components so that, for example, they again run truly with a bore previously formed. A typical example is a pair of ball-bearing housings situated at either end of a machined bore.

Here, the usual practice is to grip a length of mild steel or brass rod in the self-centring chuck and to turn it down to an interference fit in the bore of the workpiece.

Stub-mandrels made in this way are turned some ½ thou. oversize and the outer end is then eased with a fine Swiss file until, with the application of

Fig. 1

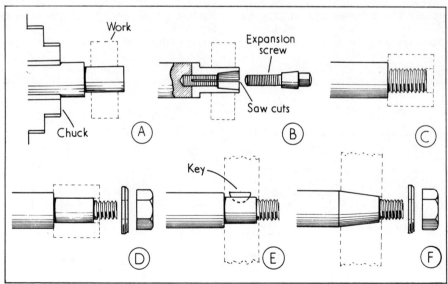

Fig. 2

moderate wringing pressure, the component can engage for a sufficient distance to obtain a satisfactory hold. The projecting end of the mandrel should be centre drilled, as for some operations the support of the tailstock may be required. After turning to size, and before the mandrel is removed from the chuck, it should be marked with a centre-punch dot exactly opposite to the centre of the face of the No. 1 jaw.

Where these mandrels have to be mounted in different chucks, it will be necessary to use the 4-jaw independent chuck rather than to rely on the self-centring pattern which usually exhibits some inaccuracy when measured over the full holding range.

The illustration Fig. 1 depicts six forms of mandrel that may be employed. The arbor (A) is the plain type we have been discussing, the work being held by friction only. At (B) one form of expanding arbor is depicted, the work being again frictionally held. (C) is a mandrel on which the work is positively secured by being screwed against a shoulder. At (D) the work is again held frictionally, a nut and washer being employed to force the work

Fig. 3

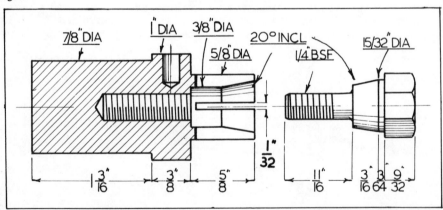

against the arbor shoulder. (E) represents an arrangement in which the work is restrained from rotation by means of a key, a nut and washer being used to secure the component endwise.

Finally (F) demonstrates an arbor sometimes used, having a tapered seating upon which the work is mounted and secured by a nut and washer, friction only securing it against rotation.

EXPANDING ARBORS

There are many types of expanding arbors designed for machining work either in the chuck or between centres, so that true running is assured.

The arbor illustrated in Fig. 2 was made for machining a set of ⅝ in. bore cast-iron change wheels, and it was found that a secure grip of the work was obtained with the application of only moderate clamping pressure.

The details of the arbor are given in Fig. 3. The turning operations needed are all straightforward, but two points may well have some emphasis. In the first place the bore of the fitting should be turned to a push fit in the components it is desired to mount, and secondly when making the expander bolt its working should be checked before it is parted off from the parent material by screwing on the arbor with a component in place. If more than moderately light pressure is needed to lock the component to the arbor, it is

advisable to ease off the apex of the screw's coned surface as that is the base which first makes contact with the coned recess. In this way, the screw will act to better mechanical advantage in expanding the arbor, as the flexible portion of the latter is quite short.

MANDRELS

Mandrels are two types, plain and expanding. Both are used for mounting work so that it may be turned between centres. Probably the most accurate are the plain mandrels, a typical example being illustrated in Fig. 4. They comprise a hardened and ground shaft, accurately centred, having a slow taper formed upon it. In order to protect them, the centres are recessed, while the small end of the mandrel is marked with an incised ring as an aid to mounting the work. A flat is also machined on the unground portion at each end to serve as an abutment point for the set screw of the lathe carrier used to drive the mandrel.

As the accuracy of mandrels mounted between centres is wholly dependent on the correct alignment of these centres, it follows that they should be in good order and that the centre set in the headstock is running true. A soft centre is supplied for fitting in the headstock as it is quite a simple matter to set over the top-slide and turn the centre true if need be.

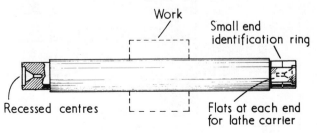

Work

Small end identification ring

Recessed centres

Flats at each end for lathe carrier

Fig. 4

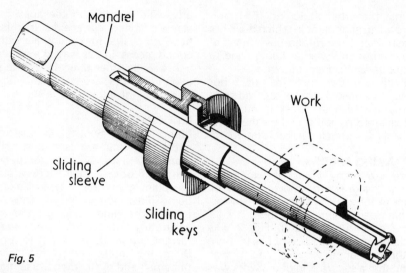

Mandrel

Work

Sliding sleeve

Sliding keys

Fig. 5

In order to cover a wide range of work size, a great number of solid mandrels are needed. To reduce the amount of equipment needed various forms of expanding mandrel have been produced, and it is probable that the example illustrated in Fig. 5 may be one of the earliest. This is the Le Count expanding mandrel, made in Canada during the first World War. The writer has two of these devices in his workshop, the smaller having a holding range of from ½ in. to 1 in., the larger of

from 1 in. to 1½ in. While not possessing the intrinsic accuracy of a plain mandrel, in view of their wide range, errors in true running have been reduced to an acceptable minimum.

The Le Count mandrels, which were bought many years ago at a trifling cost, have three undercut keyways machined in the body and these diverge radially from the axial line as they approach the base of the tool to form inclined planes. The three keys or jaws also have undercut faces so that they

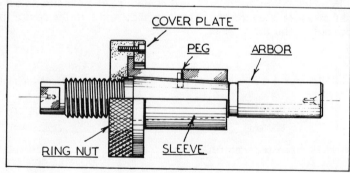

COVER PLATE

PEG

ARBOR

RING NUT

SLEEVE

Fig. 6

are retained in position as they slide in the corresponding numbered keyways.

The work faces of the jaws are stepped to enable work of various sizes to be gripped and, at the large end, a projecting tongue is formed which is engaged by the large sliding sleeve. When this sleeve is pushed towards the base of the arbor, it draws with it the sliding jaws and these expand as they are forced along the inclined keyways.

Work is secured to the mandrel by slipping it over the appropriate jaws, and the large end of the body is then lightly struck with a copper hammer until a secure hold is obtained; the work is released by driving the sleeve carefully in the opposite direction. The mandrel illustrated part-sectioned in Fig. 6 is also of the expanding type, but its range of holding is necessarily restricted. The mandrel itself consists of a hardened cone ground to a slow taper on which is mounted a hollow, split sleeve, ground parallel on its outer surface and with an internal taper corresponding to that of the mandrel itself. A register peg is fitted to the mandrel to prevent rotation of the sleeve during adjustment.

The threaded end of the mandrel carries a ring nut that serves to move the sleeve along the mandrel. For this purpose the flange machined on the end of the sleeve lies in a recess machined in the nut, and a keep-plate maintains the parts in position.

SOME SPECIAL ARBORS
In addition to the arbors that have already been described, one has sometimes to make use of types that are somewhat specialised. Of these the two screwed arbors depicted in Fig. 7 are of the single variety and were made to hold some components in the vice of a shaping machine. For this reason the

Fig. 7

shank of the arbor has a pair of flats machined upon it to ensure that it can be gripped securely and accurately in the vice jaws.

The purpose of the arbors illustrated in Fig. 8 and Fig. 9 will be clear to the reader from observing the large washers mounted on them. It will also be seen that the bodies of these arbors

Fig. 8

Fig. 9

are slotted. This is to allow the bodies to be compressed, by lightly squeezing with the vice, to ensure that the threads formed in them grip the mounting screws firmly. All shake between the two parts is thus eliminated and the washers to be chamfered will run with acceptable accuracy.

The arbor illustrated in Fig. 10 was devised to enable punched steel washers obtainable commercially to be chamfered in order to improve their appearance. The arbor consists of two parts, a body (A) and a tapered member (B) upon which the washers are moun-

ted. The end of the body is faced square with its axis, so that washers, when forced against it by the tapered member, will run true. Details of typical devices are given in Fig. 11.

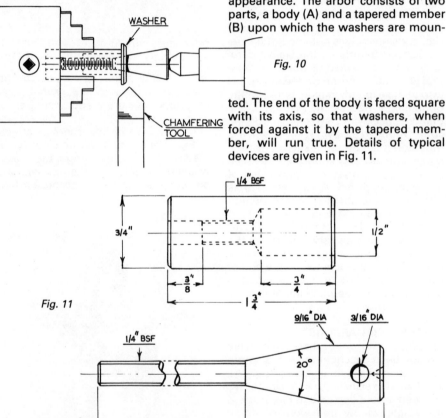

Fig. 10

Fig. 11

CHAPTER 2

BELT JOINTING AND SPLICING

Despite the widespread use of the V-rope for driving machinery of all types, flat and round belting still finds employment in connection with the older class of lathe together with any attendant overhead shafting supplied for the driving of attachments mounted on the lathe cross-slide.

In the past, leather has been the favourite material from which to make the belts and these were produced in both flat and round form. Subsequently, canvas and rubber-canvas material has been used for belt making, principally in connection with flat belting, though rubber-canvas round belts are available in endless form.

Perhaps the round belt finds its greatest use in the amateur shop, where the size of the equipment and the amount of the power to be transmitted makes this class of belt very suitable.

Round Belt Jointing Clearly, after establishing the correct diameter of belt for the drive being installed, it is essential that the joining of it should be secure and, for many workers, that the joint made should run silently.

The commonly accepted method of making the joint is to use a hook formed from steel wire and to insert this in to the belt as shown in the illustration Fig. 1.

Usually the hook is clinched over *without* any slots being first cut into the belt. This leaves the form of fastener shown standing proud, a condition conducive to a continuous clicking noise that is sometimes most irritating. If, however, the hook is clinched down into the slots then the noise level is greatly reduced if not completely eliminated.

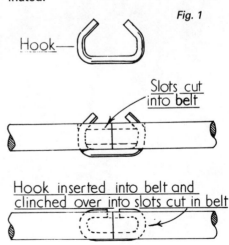

Fig. 1

Hook—

Slots cut into belt

Hook inserted into belt and clinched over into slots cut in belt

Fig. 2

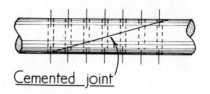

Cemented joint

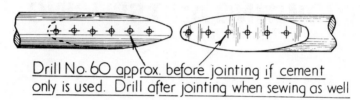

Drill No. 60 approx. before jointing if cement only is used. Drill after jointing when sewing as well

It will, of course, be appreciated that this course cannot be adopted on belts smaller than ¼ in. diameter, otherwise the belt will be unduly weakened and the fastener may pull out.

Belt Splicing If a strong silent joint is needed then the belt should be scarfed in the manner depicted by the illustration Fig. 2.

It is then cemented together with 'Durofix' or any other cellulose product; rubber-based fixatives do not seem satisfactory. The scarfing operation can be carried out in the simple fixture depicted in the illustration Fig. 3.

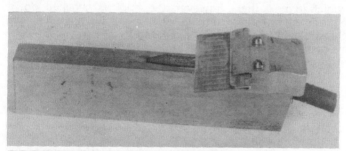

Fig. 3

Fig. 4

This consists of a block with a hole, drilled at an angle to suit the size of the belt and the slope of the scarfing needed. A razor blade set in a holder slides along the top of the block to enable the belt to be shaved. This particular fitment is not essential since the work can be carried out with a small block plane, supporting the work on a wooden board; the fixture illustrated in Fig. 4 is, however, essential. This is a clamp in which the cemented belt is inserted and held until the cementing is dry, a process taking about 24 hours. It will be apparent that the success of the clamp depends on the belt being a firm fit in it. For many purposes the finished joint will be strong enough. However, should added strength be needed then the joint can be sewn with waxed thread, using the clamp as a drill jig for the purpose.

The sewing can be either double or single, the size of the holes being selected to suit the form adopted. When making the cemented joint the ends of the belt should be wiped with a clean rag to which carbon tetrachloride or 'Thawpit' has been applied. This will remove any surface grease that may exist. The contact surfaces are then wire-brushed to roughen them before the cement is applied. In this way a good key for the 'Durofix' will be obtained and a satisfactory joint secured.

Round Rubber Belting This form of belting is commonly supplied in endless form, sewing machine belts being one example. However, if modification involving cutting the belt is needed then the only practical solution known to the author to remaking the joint is to employ the metal hook arrangement illustrated in Fig. 1.

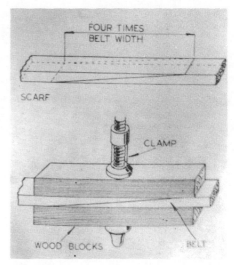

Fig. 5

Flat Belting. Flat belting is probably the oldest form to have been used. Originally made from leather, it is now fabricated from rubber-and-canvas or sometimes from laminated or folded canvas to which a bonding solution has been applied. Flat belts can be made very wide if need be, though in the amateur workshop the width is not likely to exceed three inches. Probably the most widely-used belt in the small shop was the one-inch belt. This was employed with the older type of lathe or other machine driven from lineshafting through a countershaft, the primary drive employing a 1½ in. or perhaps a 2 in. wide belt. With flat leather belting, where it is possible to employ it, the lapped and cemented joint has many advantages. It is silent and strong, when properly made, and has a working life of considerable length. An example in the author's workshop lasted 20 years, despite being liberally

15

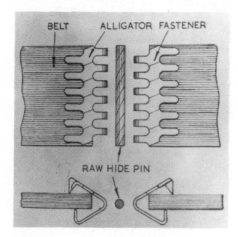

Fig. 6

Fig. 7

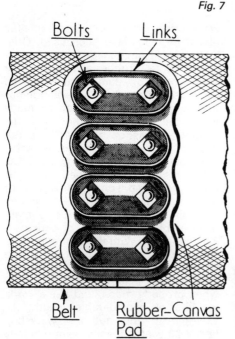

Bolts   Links

Belt   Rubber-Canvas Pad

coated with cutting oil, and it was the belt that finally broke and not the joint.

The making of cemented joints is depicted in the illustration Fig. 5. As will be noted the length of the scarf is commonly made four times the width of the belt itself. As with the round leather variety the scarf can be made with a wood plane, and pressure can be applied to the cemented joint in the manner demonstrated by the illustration.

In the past many forms of flexible jointing device have been put forward. Of these the 'Alligator' fastener seen in the illustration Fig. 6 is an example. This device consists of a series of hooks, formed from a continuous length of steel, that can be set in to the belt by hammering. A rawhide pin acts as a hinge, its seating being protected from distortion during the hammering process by the insertion of a steel pin provided for the purpose. This pin also acts as a gauge to ensure that the halves of the fastener are correctly located in relation to the ends of the belt itself, for without this provision it might subsequently be difficult to insert the rawhide pin.

The Alligator fastener, according to the sizes usually found suitable for small shops, is supplied in lengths of 6 in. and 8 in. Diagonal cuts formed in the upper surface, seen in the illustration, allow the correct length of fastener for any particular application to be broken off.

The Alligator form of fastener, by reason of the fact that it comes into direct contact with the running face of the pulley, cannot be considered as silent in operation. If silent running is required then the cemented joint is ideal, for it may be run with pulleys either in contact with its running face or

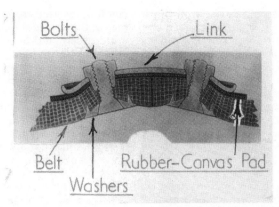

Fig. 8

on its back when a jockey pulley is fitted.

Link fasteners similar to those illustrated in Fig. 7, and in section in Fig. 8, are sometimes used to join wide belts that are to be run over comparatively large diameter pulleys. The disposition of the parts that comprise this type of fastener will be clear from the illustrations and will be seen to consist of a plate set on the back of the belt and a pair of bolts with coned washers that pass through the belt and engage nuts outside the plate itself. In service the bolts pull the washers firmly into the contact surface of the belt so that both they and the heads of the bolts themselves run clear of the pulleys; in this way a smooth silent drive is provided.

Lacing Large belts are sometimes jointed by a system of lacing using a rawhide thong for the purpose. In the small workshop, however, the process may be reproduced with copper or iron wire, which may be bedded in the belt itself and will give a strong silent join with excellent wearing qualities. For example, when jointing a one-inch belt 20 gauge copper or iron wire is used

and the stitching is carried out in accordance with the diagram Fig. 9.

After the ends of the belt have been cut square, a pencil line is drawn across the ends at a distance from the edge equal to about one-and-a-half times the

Fig. 9

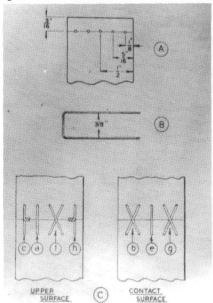

thickness of the belt and it is on these lines that the stitch holes are pierced with a scriber or a fine awl. For a one-inch belt five holes are required in either end to accommodate the two stitches used.

As represented in the drawing Fig. 9 at 'A' these holes must be evenly spaced, so that when the stitches are drawn tight the two ends of the belt come to lie truly in line.

The stitches are formed to the shape shown in Fig. 9 at 'B' preparatory to inserting them in the leather, and the successive steps in the jointing operation are as indicated in Fig. 9 at 'C'.

The first stitch is inserted from the outside of the belt as shown at (a), and then as represented at (b) the ends are crossed before being returned to the upper surface at (c).

Pull the stitch moderately tight and cross the free end to retain it in place while the second stitch is put in. This stitch is inserted from the contact surface of the belt as shown at (e), the ends are crossed, and then threaded downwards as at (f); these ends are again crossed, (g) and then brought to the upper surface of the belt as indicated at (h).

Next, pull on the ends of the stitches in turn until the ends of the belt are drawn closely together and the wire lies straight and flat. Care must be taken to draw evenly on the stitches so that the sides of the belt are brought correctly into line. The free ends of the stitches are then secured by twisting them together and afterwards cutting them off short. When the two stitches are in place, a piece of card is placed on the outer surface of the belt and the joint is compressed in the vice to embed the stitches in the running surface. If, as an alternative, the wire is struck with a hammer, it may become elongated, thus causing the joint to gape.

CHAPTER 3

SHAFT COLLARS

Clamp collars are largely used as machine fittings, usually for providing end-location of rotating spindles. For example, a lathe mandrel and the spindle of a drilling machine require some form of adjustable collar to take the reverse thrust and to eliminate play in the axial direction.

For this purpose, these machine spindles are often fitted with a pair of intersected collars, which are locked by using a couple of spanners or tommy bars after the correct adjustment has been made. However, those familiar with these fittings will have found that their action is somewhat unreliable and

Fig. 1

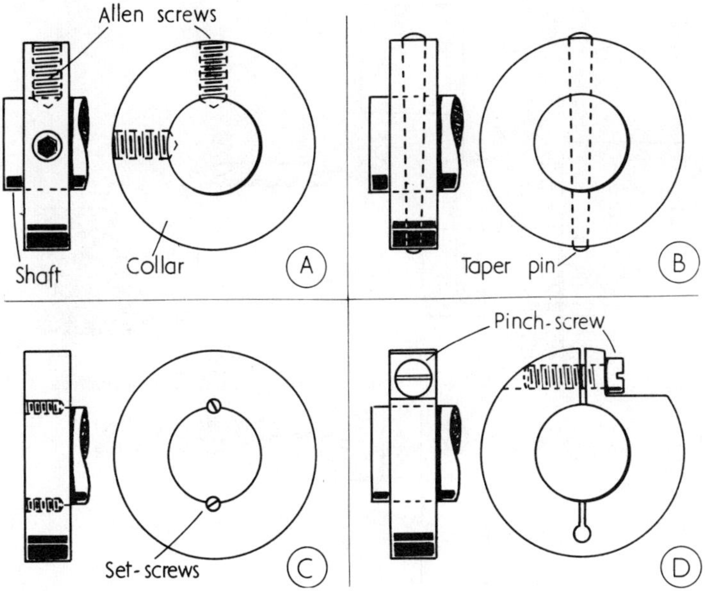

A — Allen screws, Shaft, Collar
B — Taper pin
C — Set-screws
D — Pinch-screw

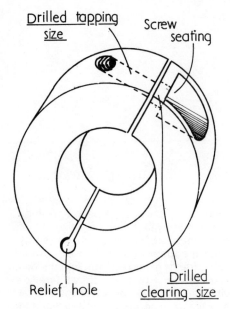

Drilled tapping size

Screw seating

Relief hole

Drilled clearing size

Fig. 2

difficult to control, for without a third hand to keep the spindle from turning, there is no certainty as to which of the two collars will turn during the final locking process. This often leads to much waste of time and effort which would not occur if the actions of adjustment and locking were independent of one another.

Non-adjustable shaft collars usually take one of the forms illustrated in Fig. 1 at A, B and C respectively, while their corresponding adjustable collar is depicted at D. Collars of this form are well adapted for fitting to plain shafts for the purpose of taking moderate thrusts or adjusting the axial working clearance. The adjustable collar shown is simple to make, needing only the simplest of machining operations, but being as it were open sided, is likely to trap rag or perhaps finger tips if either comes in contact with the collar when

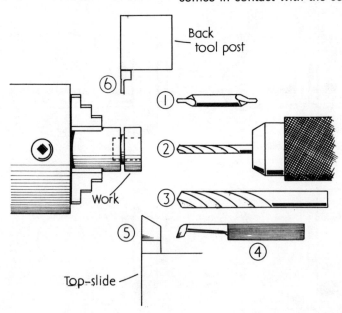

Back tool post

Work

Top-slide

Fig. 3

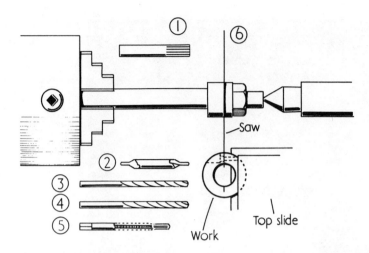

Fig. 4

rotating. The collar depicted in Fig. 2 avoids this criticism for it provides a shroud for the pinch screw that enables the collar to grip the shaft firmly.

The sequence of machining operations is set out in the operational drawings Fig. 3 and Fig. 4. It should be noted that the machined face of the collar is used as the final thrust surface as it is formed truly square with the bore; for the back surface of the collar after parting off rechucking and facing may not be accurate in this respect. Collars of this type can also be provided with a threaded bore, in which case it should be screw-cut before being parted off.

To facilitate machining operations, after parting off, the slitting operation and the formation of the screw seating should be carried out at a single setting. As depicted in the operational sequence and in Fig. 5 where the collar is in fact mounted on a block set on the cross-slide, the top-slide tool clamp is used to secure the work. Before any machining is undertaken, however, the centre line of the collar must be set at lathe centre height, packing being used for the purpose.

The proportions of clamp collars used are indicated in the accompanying table. Four sizes of collar have been included, but should larger sizes be needed their dimensions can easily be calculated, using the table as a guide.

After the collar has been correctly

Bore	Out-side dia.	Width	Slot width	Slot depth	Slot above centre	Hole dia.	Hole centre	Screw
⅜ in.	¾ in.	¼ in.	³⁄₁₆ in.	³⁄₁₆ in.	³⁄₃₂ in.	¹⁄₁₆ in.	³⁄₃₂ in.	6BA
½ in.	1 in.	⁷⁄₁₆ in.	¼ in.	⁷⁄₃₂ in.	⅛ in.	³⁄₃₂ in.	⅛ in.	6BA
⅝ in.	1¼ in.	½ in.	¼ in.	⁹⁄₃₂ in.	⁵⁄₃₂ in.	⅛ in.	³⁄₁₆ in.	2BA
¾ in.	1⅝ in.	⁹⁄₁₆ in.	⁵⁄₁₆ in.	⅜ in.	³⁄₁₆ in.	³⁄₁₆ in.	¼ in.	2BA cap

Fig. 5

mounted, the first operation is to form the recess for the head of the clamping screw with an end-mill.

The dimensions must be first determined by reference to the table. After the appropriate distance has been marked out on the collar with reference to the scribed diameter line, the saddle slides are adjusted to bring the end of the cutter into contact with the work at this point and the cross-slide index is set to zero. The machining of the recess is now carried out by a process of step-milling, until the depth is reached and the recess extends up to the scribed line indicating the distance.

While the work is still held in place, the machined abutment face of the recess is centre-drilled and afterwards drilled to the tapping size for the clamping screw. Ample clearance for the shank of this screw should be provided by counter-drilling which should extend to a point just beyond the centre line of the collar. For the tapping operation the tap is gripped in the headstock chuck and carefully fed into the work while the saddle is allowed to slide along the lathe bed.

The next operation is to cut into the bore of the collar on the diameter line by means of a circular metal saw, mounted on an arbor that can either be put between centres or gripped in the chuck and supported by the tailstock centre.

With regard to the clamping screw, it is advisable that, as a matter of safety, the head should not project above the surface of the collar. In addition, where possible, an Allen cap-screw should be fitted because when a screwdriver is pressed against an ordinary slotted screw there is always the danger of the collar turning and the fingers being injured quite apart from the loss of adjustment entailed.

An Alternative Method If preferred, to carry out most of the work, a small machine vice mounted on an angle plate can be used. This set-up has proved extremely rigid and easy to adjust. As before, all the operations to form the screw-head recess and to cut the slit are undertaken at a single setting. In this instance, however, it is not possible to machine the slit to full depth. So the work is now removed from the vice to enable the hole to be drilled in accordance with the dimensions given in the table.

The final operation is to continue the slit to meet the drill hole. This is perhaps most easily done with a fine hacksaw, but with the work reset in the machine vice it will be possible to carry the slitting to full depth if a saw of sufficiently large diameter is available.

CHAPTER 4

FINISHING METAL SURFACES

Examination of work offered to the judges at exhibitions sometimes reveals a lack of detail finish often materially detracting from the otherwise excellence of the exhibit itself. Even if one never submits a piece of work to the scrutiny of exhibition judges, the personal satisfaction of completing a well-finished product must at least be an incentive to good workmanship.

Work surfaces produced by machining processes are obvious areas that are worth critical examination to establish the quality of their finish; of these, the surfaces that result from turning work in the lathe are examples that need consideration.

TURNED WORK

If we except screw threads, surfaces produced by turning fall into two categories, the first being purely for decorative purposes, the second serving a definite engineering requirement. Of the first category the rims of flywheels or the tapered columns of steam machinery are examples, while the surface of shafts in direct contact with bearing material are examples in the second category.

Obviously, good finish on turned work depends directly on the tools used in the operation; if these are blunt or ill-formed the finish can only be poor. On the other hand, tools with a keen cutting edge, and of a form to suit the work in hand, may be expected to produce a work finish of a high standard in the decorative category. The production of such tools is a matter needing rather more treatment than there is space for here, but one cannot dismiss the matter without calling readers' attention to a basic tool form that will provide a solution to many turning problems. Much machining in the lathe involves turning up to a shoulder as well as facing the work across its end. The tool used for the purpose is called a knife tool and can be made right or left handed according to the direction from which the tool is to cut.

The tool form, which is illustrated in Fig. 1, can be applied equally well to boring tools, when a smooth finish to the work is essential.

The important feature of both these tools is the flat land that needs to be ground on the tool tip. If the tip is left with a sharp point a little consideration will show that a screw thread of very

Fig. 1

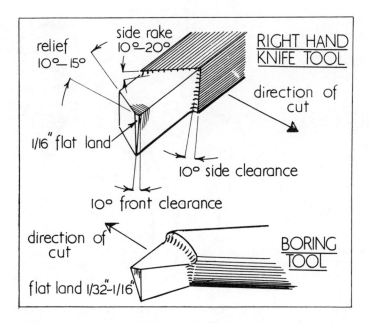

relief
10°–15°

side rake
10°–20°

RIGHT HAND
KNIFE TOOL

direction of
cut

1/16" flat land

10° side clearance

10° front clearance

direction of
cut

BORING
TOOL

flat land 1/32"–1/16"

fine pitch will be cut when the tool is moved along the surface of the work. On the other hand the flat land bridges several turns of this screw thread, thus eliminating them and so producing a smooth finish.

This principle is applied when using the tool illustrated in Fig. 2. This device, which is known as the Spring Tool, bridges a large surface of the work, again eliminating any ridging produced by the initial turning operations. The tool itself is of some antiquity and the results produced by it are nowadays achieved by other means. When using a spring tool the work must be turned slowly and the amount of cut should be minimal, up to a maximum of 0.005 in. for example. Today, the spring tool really belongs to history, though the author has sometimes used it in his shaping machine where it can give a good account of itself.

Formerly the spring tool was employed to finish-turn areas that were to be run in plain bearings. Present practice, but not necessarily in commercial undertakings, is to make use of the process known as 'lapping.'

Meanwhile, we had better return to the decorative finishing of machine surfaces. Of these the flywheel rim pre-

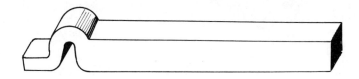

Fig. 2

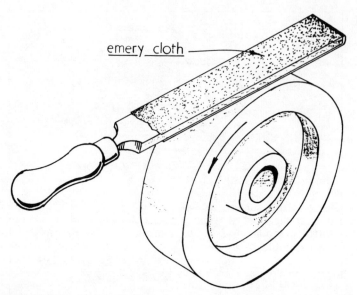

emery cloth

Fig. 3

viously mentioned will serve as an example. It is seldom that the finish imparted to the rim by turning alone is sufficiently good to pass muster. So one must, even after using a spring tool, sometimes have recourse to the practice illustrated in Fig. 3. Here a piece of aloxite or emery cloth is wrapped around a flat file and is applied to the rim. Previously, however, it is sometimes well first to use a Swiss file on the revolving work. A Swiss file, that is one of very fine cut, will reduce the work surface more quickly than coarse

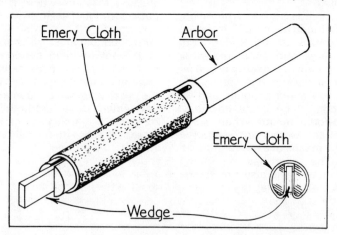

Emery Cloth

Arbor

Emery Cloth

Wedge

Fig. 4

emery to a point where medium and finally fine abrasive cloth can be used. Do not use the emery dry but apply some thin lubricating oil to the cloth. This will prevent clogging and enable the abrasive to cut more freely.

POLISHING INTERNAL SURFACES

It is sometimes necessary to polish the surface of work bored in a component. In some cases, the work can be rotated in the lathe, in others it remains stationary whilst the polishing medium is rotated within it. Unless the bore is of large diameter and the surface to be treated narrow, application of emery cloth on the end of an index finger is not possible. Indeed, it could be positively dangerous.

Instead, the device illustrated in Fig. 4 can be used mounted in the lathe tailstock chuck.

This tool consists of an arbor split longitudinally and provided with a wedge to expand it. As seen in the end-on view of the device, emery cloth is wrapped around the arbor and has its ends tucked into the saw cut. In use oil is applied to the abrasive surface and the device is traversed in and out of the work by means of the tailstock. When the latter is provided with a lever feed the operation is greatly simplified.

A fitment supplied by Messrs. Black & Decker may also be used for polishing the bore of a component. Primarily designed to be rotated at speed in an electric hand drill the device consists of a rubber set on an arbor and able to be expanded by means of a nut running on the arbor. The arbor has a standing flange riveted to it and a second flange that moves axially under the influence of the nut. The rubber hub is caught between the washers and is caused to expand by the nut, so gripping the abra-

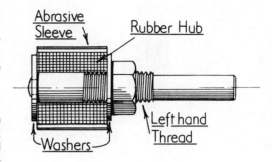

Fig. 5

sive sleeves with which the device is furnished. The range of expansion is necessarily somewhat limited but the author has used the fitments both with work rotating in the lathe and with components held in the hand whilst the polisher is revolved by the electric drill.

The parts of the Black & Decker device are illustrated in Fig. 5. Three sizes are available for sleeves ½ in., ¾ in. and 1 inch diameter respectively. In all cases the shank of the arbors is ¼ in. diameter.

FINISHING FLAT SURFACES

In the first instance flat surfaces on metal work are produced either by filing or by a machining operation. When filing is the method employed it is important that in the final stages the file should be applied in one direction only, using a fine cut file in the last stages of the process. In this way the finished surface will be smooth, with the lines of the file cuts parallel. It is advisable to apply light machine oil to the work in order to prevent the file 'pinning', so spoiling the finished surface.

When filing is employed to finish narrow surfaces such as the edges of work, the practice known as 'draw-filing'

27

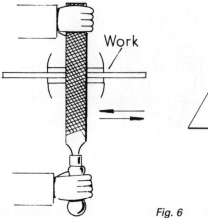

Work

Fig. 6

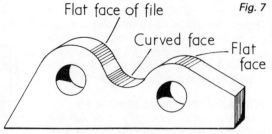

Flat face of file   Fig. 7

Curved face   Flat face

the normal procedure of applying the file to work held in the vice.

The file itself can be secured either by being gripped in the vice, pieces of card being interposed to protect the vice jaws, or it may be mounted on a board as indicated in the illustration Fig. 8. A large flat file, 16 in. long or more, of medium or fine cut, has its tang first removed by sawing. It is then set on the board and is prevented from movement endwise by wooden keeps screwed down at each end. Since the file itself is double sided, and the work to be treated may be both ferrous and non-ferrous, the file should be marked with paint on one side so that this face can be kept for brass working.

From the illustration it will be noticed that a leather tab is provided so that the

should be used. As will be seen from the diagram Fig. 6, the workman grips a flat file at each end and, having set it at right angles to the axis of the work, draws it backwards and forwards along the surface. If the work surface is curved, as depicted in Fig. 7, a half-round file must be used and applied to the work as indicated in the illustration.

THE FILING BOARD

When the surface of small components is being treated it is often better to take the work to the file rather than to adopt

Fig. 8

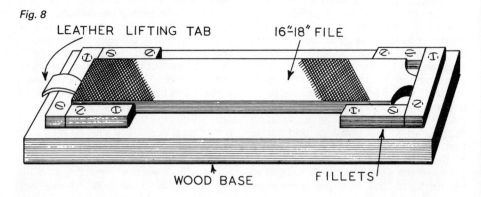

LEATHER LIFTING TAB   16"–18" FILE

WOOD BASE   FILLETS

Fig. 9

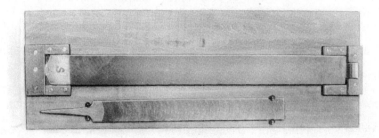

file can be lifted and turned over the more easily when needed.

The example of the filing board in the author's workshop may be seen in the illustration Fig. 9 and the marking on the base of the file should be clearly seen. In addition there is a second file specifically intended for use with aluminium alloys. As many readers will be aware, these alloys are sometimes difficult to work with ordinary files, though by chalking the file one may reduce, if not completely inhibit, the 'pinning' that sometimes results. In use, work is placed on the surface of the file and is pushed along it in the direction of the cut, care being taken to see that the part being treated maintains a straight line and is not allowed to wander about.

SCRAPING

The process of scraping is used for two purposes. Firstly it may be employed to ensure that the work is truly flat, the part being tested by reference to a surface plate where any high spots are indicated by blue marking that has previously been applied to the surface plate itself.

The blue marking is scraped off, taking off a small portion of the surface in the process. As the operation proceeds,

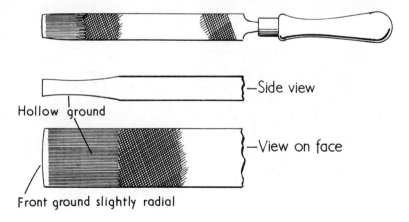

—Side view

Hollow ground

—View on face

Fig. 10   Front ground slightly radial

and as a result, the area of blue markling that is transferred to the work gradually increases, the flatness of the surface gradually improves until the marking is seen to cover the whole of the area. The work is then considered flat.

The second use is for decorative purposes, i.e. applying a finish which is attractive and may embody other advantages, but before discussing the process of scraping as a purely decorative procedure we must first consider the tool form that will produce it.

The Flat Scraper Scrapers come in three forms, half-round, triangular and flat, according to the nature of the work they are to do, but in this instance it is the flat scraper with which we are concerned. While one may buy such scrapers in a tool shop, most workers prefer to make their own from an old worn file. Many believe, and the author is amongst them, that scrapers made from this source maintain the keeness of the cutting edge much longer than do the commercially-made tools. The flat scraper itself is depicted in the illustration Fig. 10, where it will be seen to have its faces slightly hollow ground while the front edge is rounded also by a grinding operation.

Making a Flat Scraper To make the scraper the front of the file is first rounded as depicted in Fig. 11 and the hollow-grinding is then imparted to its lower faces as already indicated. In this connection it pays to blunt all the teeth of the file by passing it across the grinding wheel, otherwise the rough surface is liable, during prolonged working, to make the hands sore.

Once the grinding operations are complete, the scraper is transferred to the oilstone. First the cutting edges are honed as illustrated in Fig. 12 at 'A'. Next, the front is honed to remove any wire edge, the scraper being rocked in the direction of the arrows seen in Fig. 12 at 'B'. Finally, a light honing on a fine oilstone, such as Washita or Arkansas stone, in the direction depicted at 'C'

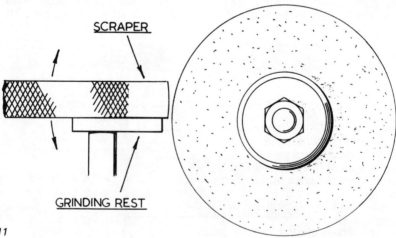

SCRAPER

GRINDING REST

Fig. 11

Fig. 12

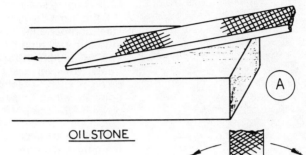

SCRAPER

OILSTONE

A

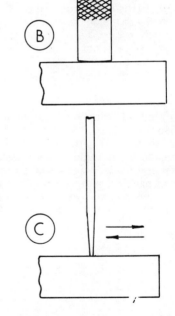

B

C

will help to put a fine edge to the scraper.

FROSTING

At one time, inspecting of the beds of lathes, the vertical faces of milling machine columns and similar machined surfaces would display to the viewer ornamental patterns of some complexity that had been produced by hand-scraping with a tool of the type that has just been described.

These patterns need much practice and not a little skill to produce them, so it is perhaps hardly surprising that few amateur workers are prepared to give time to mastering the technique. One should, perhaps, explain that the process, apart from providing a pleasing appearance, has the effect of breaking up the work surface so that it would hold oil the more easily. Today, however, many of the surfaces referred to earlier are finished by a grinding process while it is the mating slides that have their surfaces broken up by the scraping operation. As this takes place in areas that are not seen no pattern is needed.

If effective but simple ornamentation is needed one may perhaps call readers' attention to the device of 'frosting'. This is an ornamenting process imported to the work by the flat scraper. An example of the result is illustrated in Fig. 13 where frosting as applied to a small surface plate is depicted.

Fig. 13

The method employed is as seen in the diagram Fig. 14. The flat scraper is applied to the work with its cutting edge maintained at an angle and a series of passes are made across the surface. Short strokes crossing each other are made in the way shown, and the angle at which the scraper is used is much the

Fig. 14

Result

Direction of
1st pass

Direction of
2nd pass

same as that employed when its cutting edge is being sharpened.

If the 'frosting' is to be carried out on steel components it is well to apply a little thin machine oil to their surfaces. This will enable the scraper to cut more freely. However, cast iron parts need no oiling as such a practice would have the opposite effect and reduce the cutting power of the scraper.

ENGINE TURNING

A method once used for decorating a metal surface is 'Engine Turning'. This, as may be seen in the illustration Fig. 15, consists of making a series of circu-

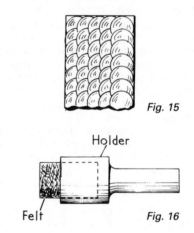

Fig. 15

Holder

Felt   Fig. 16

lar abraded marks on the work whose surface has first been made smooth by machining or by filing.

The operation is performed in the drilling machine with a felt 'dolly' set in a holder of the type depicted in Fig. 16. The dolly is saturated with oil and is impregnated with an abrasive compound such as one of the lapping media consisting of carborundum grains suspended in oil. The size of the grains used will be dictated by the work itself. Obviously large work surfaces can take a coarser finish than would a small one, and the diameter and pitch of the pattern used will also depend on the size of the components to be treated.

As will be seen from the illustration Fig. 17, the pattern is composed of circles that are spaced half-a-diameter apart. While it is not difficult to keep to this spacing free-hand, it is as well to set up a simple fence on the drilling machine to ensure that the circles are kept on a straight line. When carrying out this form of decoration the surface of the work itself has the abrasive com-

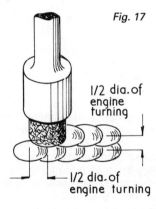

Fig. 17

1/2 dia. of engine turning

1/2 dia. of engine turning

pound spread thinly on it. In this way the dolly is kept well impregnated with abrasive and the pattern produced is of uniform density. When the work has been completed the abrasive should be *washed* off the surface, not wiped off or the work may be spoilt as a result of the pattern becoming blurred.

Perhaps it is worth mentioning that when no hard felt is available, a cork may be used as a dolly provided the work is not extensive. Cork used in this way has only a short life and is likely to

break up if subjected to sustained loading.

FINISHING BOLTS, NUTS AND SCREWS

An otherwise well-finished piece of work is sometimes spoilt by the appearance of the screws or other fixings used to hold the parts together. Commercial bolts, nuts and screws for the most part do not receive any further surface finishing other than that already imparted by the machines used to produce them. It follows, therefore, that the quality of this finish, although adequate for general purposes, is not likely to be of exhibition standard, or even to satisfy the critical eye of the constructor himself.

Hexagon-head bolts should be treated in the manner depicted by the illustration Fig. 18. The end-face of the bolt head, which is seldom flat and often has a 'pip' left by the parting-off operation, needs to be faced, while the flat surfaces of the hexagon head itself should be cleaned up with a fine Swiss file, the direction of the strokes being made along the axis of the bolt.

If the opposite end of the bolt is on view when assembled with its companion nut it should be either machined or filed while rotating in the lathe as indicated in Fig. 19 at 'A' and 'B' respectively.

The procedure adopted will, of course, depend upon the way the bolt

Face

Fig. 18

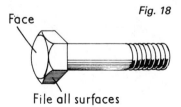

File all surfaces

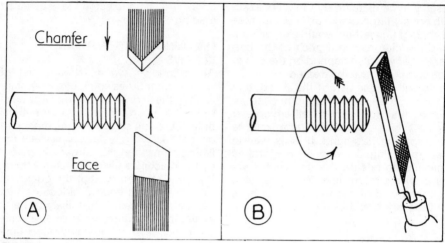

Fig. 19

itself has been machined to provide a lead for the screwing die.

Round-head screws are sometimes used to secure pieces of mechanism together. For the most part round-headed screws seem to have their head surfaces rather better machined than other screws so any correction to them

Fig. 20

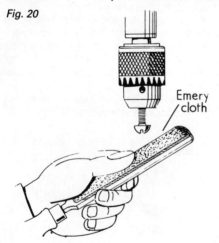

Emery cloth

can usually be made by the application of emery cloth in the manner depicted by the illustration Fig. 20.

Some screws with countersunk heads, in particular those that have cut threads as opposed to rolled threads, are well enough finished to be left alone. In others, however, the head is roughened and needs to be polished. This may be done by holding the screw in the drill chuck as seen in the previous illustration, then, by using the machine's feed lever, bringing the head of the rotating screw into contact with a fine file set on the table of the drilling machine, Fig. 21. A thin piece of card is interposed between the file and the table to prevent the latter being marked and a little light machine oil is applied to the surface of the file to stop it from 'pinning' and spoiling the work.

If a high finish on the work is needed the filing operation can be followed by the application of a smooth oilstone used in the same way as the file has been.

34

Fig. 21

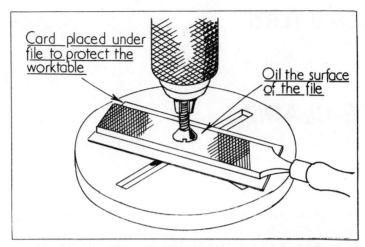

Card placed under file to protect the worktable

Oil the surface of the file

Instrument head screws, sometimes called countersunk-round head screws, need to be treated in the same way as the round-head screws described.

Finishing Nuts Since nuts are, for the most part, made from bright drawn material, their flat surfaces need to be filed in the same way as those of hexagon-head bolts and screws. Fortunately, nuts may be treated in batches if they are mounted on suitable bolts as illustrated in Fig. 22.

Whilst this assemblage *can* be gripped in the jaws of the bench vice, using pieces of card to protect the corners of the nuts, it may be difficult to ensure perfect alignment of the surfaces to be filed. However, the use of the fixture illustrated in Fig. 23 will ensure that the nuts are correctly presented. This fixture, of course, is set in the vice jaws; it grips the nuts, aligning them automatically, so that a series of flat faces is presented horizontally for the filing process.

Fig. 22

Fig. 23

CHAPTER 5

G-CLAMPS

The G-clamp is one of the oldest tools in the workshop and certainly is one of the most useful. It serves, for example, to hold two pieces of work together while they are fastened to one another.

While there is no lack of large clamps in the tool shops, it seems that it is not possible to buy the small G-clamps so useful in model making and work of a similar nature, so the obvious solution is for the worker to make them for himself.

The common pattern of clamp is illustrated in Fig. 1. Usually the frame is a steel forging having a clamp screw passing through it. At one time, however, a cheaper variety was available; these had frames of malleable iron or even of cast iron. The clamps were not to be despised for, within the limits imposed by the strength of the materials used in their construction, they were capable of much useful service.

In most cases, there is a foot attached

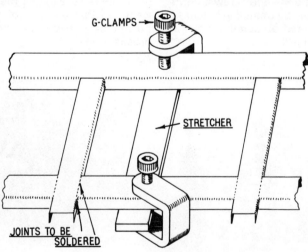

G-CLAMPS

STRETCHER

JOINTS TO BE SOLDERED

Fig. 1

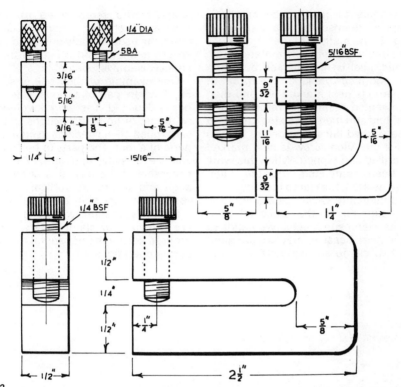

Fig. 2

to the clamp screw in order to prevent damage to the work, especially if made of wood. It is advisable therefore, in the interest of good workmanship, to interpose a piece of packing between the work and the foot, since the latter is seldom smooth enough to avoid marking the work.

Large G-clamps are of little use in connection with the small components encountered in model making and there are, apparently, no strong small size clamps to be had in the tool shops. Fortunately they are easily made either from scrap parts, such as large nuts, or from suitable pieces of material.

A number of these simple devices is illustrated in Fig. 2; as will be seen, the clamp screws are, for the most part, standard Allen cap screws. No footing to the screws is provided as this would take up valuable space and protection for the work can equally well if not better be assured by the introduction of some packing between the end of the screw and the part itself. The one on the left is a clamp made from one old ¾ in. Whitworth square nut; nuts of this type and size can often be obtained from the local blacksmith or agricultural engineer.

In order to provide information enabling readers to make such small G-clamps for themselves details are given in Fig. 2. The method of making them is very simple – a piece of material such as mild steel is first marked out, then sawn and filed to shape. The throat of the clamp is next marked out and then all unwanted material is removed first by drilling and then by sawing and filing to the scribed lines. The centre hole to receive the Allen screw is next marked out, drilled and tapped. When this work has been completed and the Allen screw inserted, the clamp is ready.

The miniature G-clamps are in many ways superior to the so-called tool-makers' clamps that need two hands to adjust them, because they are provided with two clamp screws instead of the single clamp screw fitted to the G-clamps. There are many occasions when the user has only one hand free to secure a clamp, and it is then that the small G-clamp is invaluable.

One example of their use is seen in Fig. 1 where part of a model side member is depicted. The work involved the soldering of tin-plate sections to represent rolled steel channels used in some parts of a tool. The parts to be soldered will be readily apparent. Each has necessitated the use of a stretcher to align and secure the vertical and horizontal members while being soldered.

Naturally, though two G-clamps only are shown, four clamps were used in order to secure the horizontal members during operations.

CHAPTER 6

SURFACE GAUGES AND RULE HOLDERS

The composite title of this chapter need not come as any surprise, for the two pieces of equipment are used together, the surface gauge for scribing centre or dimension lines on work set up on the surface table, the rule holder to enable the surface gauge to be set to any required dimension by holding the rule itself truly upright.

Surface gauges are for the most part a normal commercial supply. Rule holders, for some reason or another, do not seem to be so and if he needs one the worker must therefore make the device for himself. In the past both the author and others have described several types of rule holder, and some of these will form subjects for detailed description later.

THE SURFACE GAUGE
The surface gauge appears in several forms, three of these being seen in the illustrations Figs. 1, 2 & 3.

The first is a simple gauge having a round base and a fixed pillar; its simple design makes it very suitable for construction by the amateur worker who will find it a good general purpose tool.

The second gauge, depicted in Fig. 2, was designed in the Cambridge Univer-

sity workshops, presumably as a useful exercise for engineering students; the example shown was made by the author using a drawing that appeared in a book entitled 'Workshop Practice for School and Laboratory' by A. W. Barker and A. H. Chapman, published in 1927.

Fig. 1

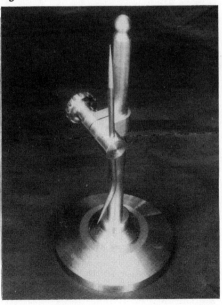

mechanism consists of a plunger C through which is passed the spindle of the scriber mount D. The fine adjustment is controlled by a finger nut on the top of the block moving the plunger against the pressure of a return spring. The block is secured to the pillar by a half-moon collar that can be locked by the finger nut seen to the left of the block. All the fine-adjustment parts mentioned are illustrated in Fig. 5.

While this surface gauge might be described as a universal device, the gauge depicted earlier in the illustration Fig. 3 is a commercial Universal Surface Gauge made by James Neill of Sheffield. Its parts are similar to and perform

Fig. 3

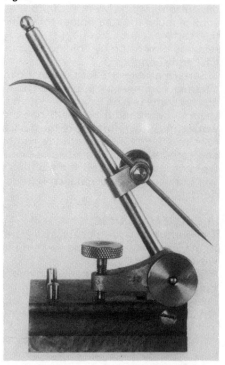

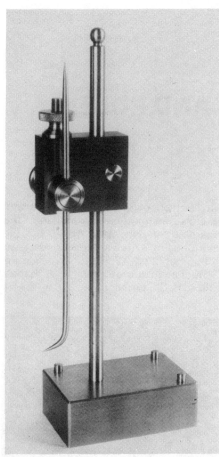

Fig. 2

The design is somewhat unusual, including as it does an arrangement that provides for a fine adjustment to the scriber point. The parts comprising this surface gauge are depicted in the sectional illustration Fig. 4. The base A forms a mounting for the pillar supporting the block B in which the fine-adjustment mechanism is housed. The

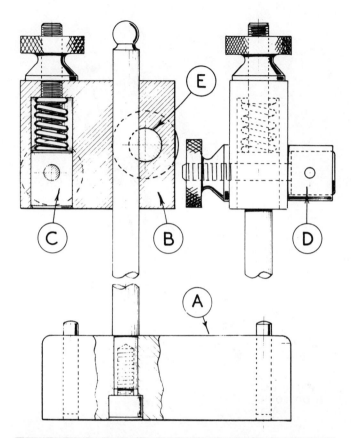

Fig. 4

Fig. 5

41

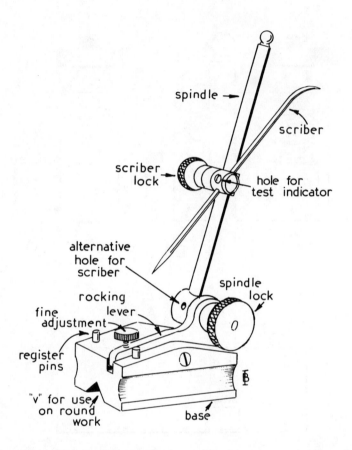

spindle →

scriber

scriber lock

hole for test indicator

alternative hole for scriber

rocking lever

spindle lock

fine adjustment

register pins

"v" for use on round work

base

Fig. 6

the same functions as the components illustrated in Fig. 6, depicting the type of surface gauge made by Browne & Sharp or L. S. Starret of America. The illustration should itself be sufficient explanation as to the use and disposition of the various parts that make up the complete surface gauge. Perhaps a word or two should be said about the friction hinges that are fitted to control both the spindle and the scriber. Obviously some restraint needs to be imposed on both these details when setting the gauge, or adjustment of the

scriber would be impossible. Here, again, the illustration Fig. 7 should explain itself. The important component is the spring that puts pressure on the coned distance piece and so causes the draw bolt to rotate stiffly.

The Register Pins It will be observed that the bases of two of the surface gauges are fitted with pins that can be pushed down to act as guides for the base. These enable a worker, for example, to scribe lines actually on work mounted on the lathe. To this end the

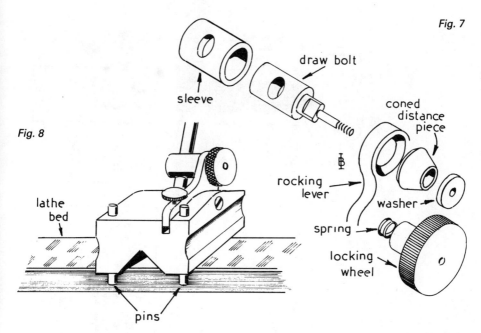

Fig. 7

draw bolt

sleeve

coned distance piece

Fig. 8

rocking lever

lathe bed

washer

spring

locking wheel

pins

pins are made to protrude so that they engage the edge of the lathe bed as illustrated in Fig. 8.

A MINIATURE SURFACE GAUGE

While it is perfectly possible to use the base of the standard surface gauge or the head of the Cambridge device to hold the scriber directly, some may consider that the provision of a miniature gauge, or scribing block to give it another name, is justifiable. Obviously its range is limited, but if one is working on a small surface plate, with, perhaps, other pieces of equipment occupying some space, a miniature surface gauge has advantages.

The little scribing block depicted in Fig. 9 was produced with these observations in view. Its working parts are to be seen in Fig. 10. They comprise a base (1) through which passes a spindle (4)

supporting the scriber area (8) and the scriber (7). The scriber point is set for height by turning the height adjustment knob (2).

In order to ensure some restraint that will prevent the scriber from shifting during the adjustment process the

Fig. 9

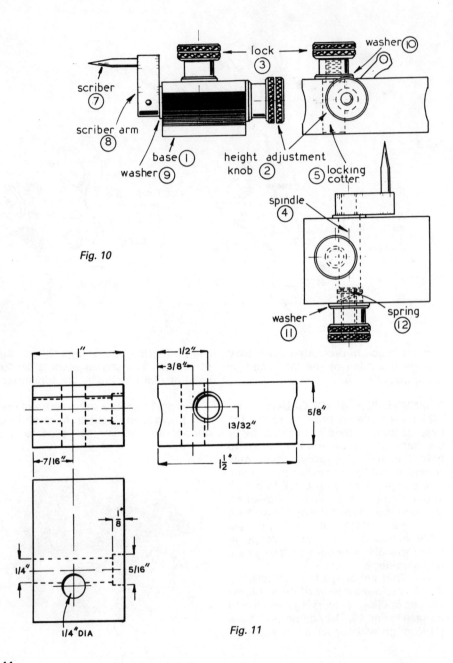

scriber ⑦

scriber arm ⑧

lock ③

washer ⑩

base ①

washer ⑨

height adjustment knob ②

locking cotter ⑤

spindle ④

washer ⑪

spring ⑫

Fig. 10

1"

7/16"

1/2"

3/8"

13/32"

1½"

5/8"

1/8"

1/4"

5/16"

1/4"DIA

Fig. 11

spindle (4) is subjected to friction by the spring (12) acting against the washer (11).

Once the scriber has been set it has to be locked. This requirement is satisfied by the locking cotter (5) which is actuated by the lock (3).

Details of the base are given in Fig. 11 while the particulars of the remaining components are to be seen in Fig. 12.

RULE HOLDERS

To obtain the maximum service from a surface gauge on the marking-off table a rule holder is essential. Provided that one only needs to mount a small 3–4 in-rule the simple holder depicted in Fig. 13 will probably suffice. From the illustrations it should be clear that its construction is of the simplest possible. It is important to make sure that the rule itself is held firmly and that it remains upright when the holder is in use, so the leaf spring clip secures the rule while the two pins seen in the illustration serve as a register to keep it upright. These details may be seen in Fig. 14.

Some years ago the L. S. Starret Company of America introduced a form of rule holder designed to accommodate a wide range of rules. The Starret Rule Holder depicted in Fig. 15 has a firm base enabling rules 12 in. long to be mounted securely while Starret's

Fig. 12

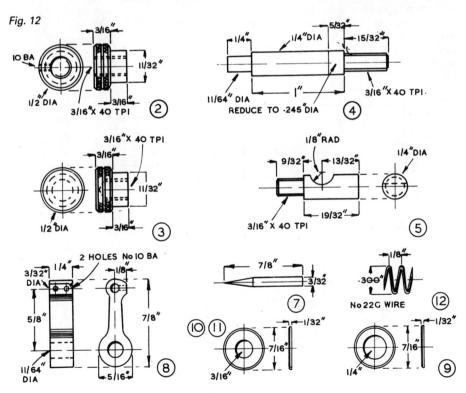

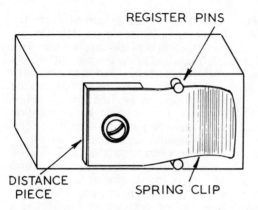

REGISTER PINS

DISTANCE
PIECE

SPRING CLIP

Fig. 13

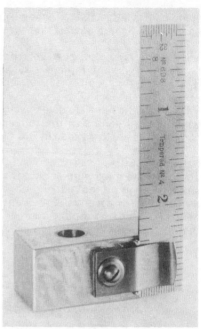

own 3 inch rules, which are only ⁹⁄₁₆ in.
wide, can be set in the holder.

In view of the apparent non-
availability of the Starret device the
author, needing a rule holder of similar
capacity, made for himself the mounting base illustrated in Fig. 16. This piece

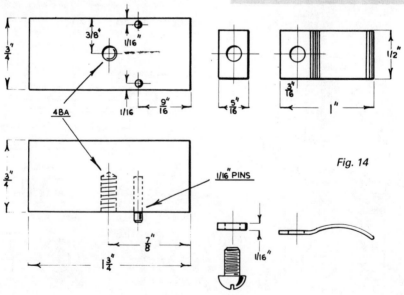

Fig. 14

Fig. 15

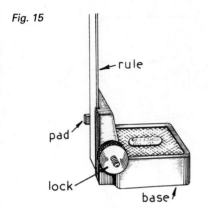

rule

pad

lock

base

Fig. 16

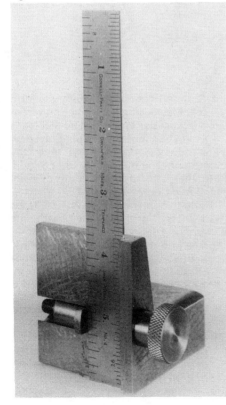

Fig. 17

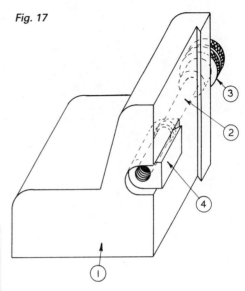

of equipment has a base machined from mild steel with details made from the same material. The general arrangements of the device are depicted in Fig. 17. The base (1) has a dovetailed abutment machined on its vertical face, and it is against this abutment that the edge of the rule impinges. The rule is held in place by the block (4). This part has a dovetail machined upon it to register with the opposite edge of the rule and it is pulled into contact with the rule by means of the threaded spindle (2) and its knurled finger grip (3).

Of the machining involving the small details, little need be said. The measurements of these parts are given in Fig. 19 and the work includes no difficult process. The base, however, needs some comment. The part is made from a 2 in. cube of mild steel that is marked off in accordance with the details given in Fig. 18. The sequence of

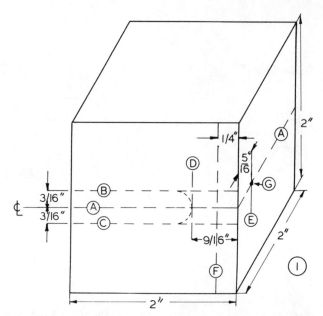

Fig. 18

operations for marking off and machining is as follows:
(1) Scribe the centre line AA 1 inch from the base of the cube on two sides as shown.
(2) At right angles to this line and 5/16 in. from the front face of the cube scribe the line E. Where the line E cuts the centre line AA centre-punch the junction G. This is the centre for the axis of the spindle seating and that of the block (4).
(3) Centre drill, pilot drill and ease the spindle seating 3/16 in. dia. using a no. 15 drill as the pilot. Carry this hole through to the opposite side of the cube so that it may also act as a pilot for the block seating.
(4) Pilot drill for the 3/8 in. dia. clamping piece seating using a 11/32 in. dia. drill fed into the work for 1 7/16 in. as measured to the drill point.
(5) Open out the seating to 3/8 in. dia.

(6) Counterbore base of seating to form a flat face using a spotface cutter (or a long series end-mill if available).

The seating for the clamping piece (4) must now be machined to meet the diameter of the previously drilled 3/8 in. hole, that is to say, to a depth of 5/16 in. measured from the front face.

To do this the block needs, first, to be marked off in accordance with the illustration Fig. 18 already mentioned.
(1) Carry the centre line A already scribed on the side face of the block through to its face and scribe 3/16 in. from this line two others B and C above and below it. These two lines represent the confines of the slot to be drilled.
(2) Scribe the line D 3/16 in. from the edge of the block. This represents the point at which the end-milling operation must stop.
(3) Set the block on the cross-slide

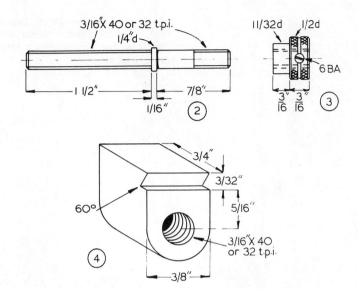

Fig. 19

packed up till the line A coincides with the centre line of the lathe, and with the face of the block truly at right angles to this line. Clamp firmly and machine with a ⅜ in. end mill set to run true in the 4-jaw chuck or in a collet mounted on the lathe mandrel.

To form the undercut abutment shoulder against which the rule rests the following procedure must be carried out:

(1) Scribe the line F ¼ in. from the side of the block.

(2) Mount the block on the cross-slide with the line F lying horizontally and facing the headstock.

(3) Carry out the machining either with an angular cutter or a fly cutter mounted at an angle.

(4) If a fly-cutter is used the toolpoint must be ground and finally stoned to an "inverted bevel" of 60 deg. point angle. The point is then set to the dimension line F and the cutter

used to cut back the face of the block for a distance of ³⁄₃₂ in.

(5) To form the undercut back the work away and set out the fly-cutter so that the radius on which the tip lies is increased by ³⁄₃₂ in.

(6) The work is now brought up so that the tool's cutting edge exactly touches the previously machined surface. A final cut is now taken with a very slow feed right across the work surface.

Remember that the lathe saddle should be firmly clamped during the machining operations, and that if there is a power feed to the cross-slide this should be used.

AN ADJUSTABLE RULE HOLDER

The rule holder illustrated in Figs. 20 and 21 was given to the writer many years ago and clearly dates from the time when the repetition making of parts involved 'marking-off', often a simple process but sometimes a com-

49

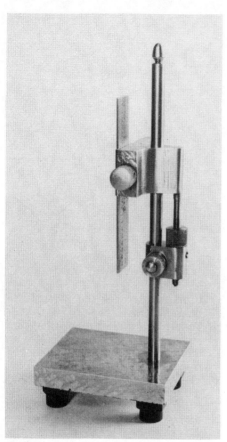

not always in the small professional shop. The rule holder illustrated therefore may be not without interest to some readers.

Fig. 21

Fig. 20

plicated one. In the latter event a rule holder to be used in conjunction with a surface gauge was essential. If the rule in the holder was capable of adjustment so that it could be set to a convenient reading from which other dimensions could be read off so much the better. Today, when it is required, this work is largely performed with a vernier height gauge, an expensive tool not often found in the amateur workshop, and

Fig. 22

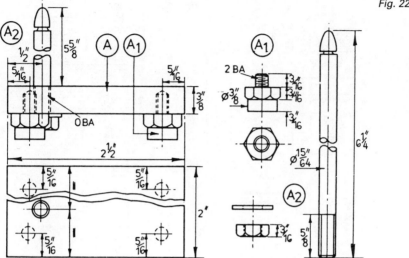

The device consists of but three major parts, the base A provided with four feet A1 and a pillar A2 to support the rule clamp B and an anchorage C for the fine adjustment components. The base A is made from a piece of mild steel ⅜ in. thick and 2 in. by 2 inch. The four feet, the dimensions of which are given in the drawing Fig. 22, are made from hexagon material and are secured to the base itself by being screwed into threaded holes. The pillar, threaded at its lower extremity, is secured by a nut and washer on the underside of the base.

The rule holder itself is designed to be adjustable not only for the height at which the rule itself is to be set, but also for the width of any rules that may be needed. The rule holder body (B) is therefore provided with a moving jaw (B1) actuated by the adjusting screw (B2) both seen in Fig. 23. The dimensions of the holder and its component parts allow rules from ½ in. wide to 1 in.

wide to be grasped firmly. The elevating screw (B3), also seen in Fig. 23, is set in the underside of the rule holder body and is operated by the adjustment nut (C1) placed in a recess on the top surface of the anchorage (C). For some reason or other the elevating screw was given a left hand thread. The advantages of this are not easily understood since it seems the device can function equally well with a right hand thread. The anchorage is fixed to the pillar (A2) by the clamp bolt (C2) tension being imparted by the barrel nut (C3).

With regard to the centring of the adjusting screw (B2) I have had difficulty in determining this without undertaking some further dismantling that might prove unpropitious. However, anyone contemplating the making of this device will no doubt make use of the rule clamp body as a jig, after marking-off, drilling and reaming ³⁄₁₆ in. dia. for the 2 BA screw itself. I had not intended to provide a blow-by-blow

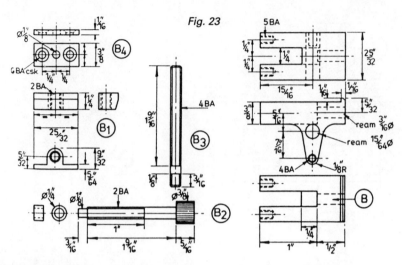

Fig. 23

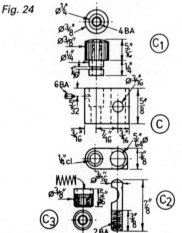

Fig. 24

instruction on making the rule holder for the good reason that I myself did not make it, and anyone who may contemplate its construction will scarcely need lessons in the simple work involved. As will be seen, the adjusting screw (B2) is provided with a small collar to hold the screw in place. This is cross-pinned to the screw itself, an ordinary sewing pin will serve well here.

A word or two about the clamp bolt C2. My method of dealing with the problem of producing accurately the radial recess in the clamp bolt would be to machine a head on the bolt itself. This of course is made larger than the body of the bolt so that, when the latter is placed in the anchorage and secured by its accompanying nut, the hole for the pillar A2 can be marked off for drilling and reaming to size. Once this is done the oversize portion of the clamp bolt can be turned off leaving the desired clamping effect in operation.

With regard to the end plate B4, make sure that the countersinks for the fixing screws allow the screw heads to be flush. If they are not the collar on the adjusting screw B2 will be displaced. Incidentally, it may be as well to use the end plate itself as a drill jig when drilling for the fixing holes in the rule holder B. To this end all the parts of the device should be assembled in place and this end plate clamped firmly in place when all is seen to work smoothly.

52

CHAPTER 7

CUTTING HOLES IN SHEET METAL AND PLATE

Many pieces of metalwork involve the cutting of holes of various shapes and sizes in the parts that comprise the work. While the expert finds no difficulty in carrying out the operations needed to produce the holes, the novice finds their production something of a problem and is often very unsure as to how to go about it.

In the past there have been many tools designed to cut circular holes in sheet material of one form or another. Most of these were intended for use in hand-operated devices such as carpen-ter's braces; they have, in some cases, been re-designed to fit them for use in machines, particularly in hand-held drilling equipment. As a matter of history, the tools illustrated in Fig. 1 and Fig. 2 were intended for use in the carpenter's brace, their purpose being to cut large holes in metal plate (Fig. 1), and then sheet or jointing material (Fig. 2), the last device being capable of producing a complete plug at one operation.

Both tools are provided with pilots, holes for which must be drilled before

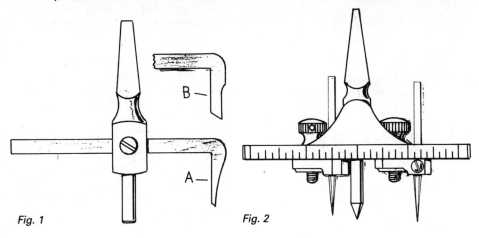

Fig. 1   Fig. 2

Fig. 3

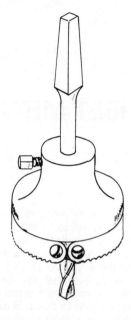

Fig. 4

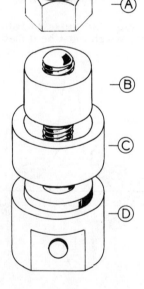

the tools themselves can be used, and it is around these pilots that the tools are rotated to cut any aperture that may be required.

The tool illustrated in Fig. 3 is, perhaps, also more of historic than of practical interest, though it appears, still, in some tool merchants' catalogues. Its construction will be obvious from the illustration in that it consists of a pilot drill supporting a hub that serves as a mount for a length of hacksaw blade. Tools of this type are often called tank cutters, work which they can perform a deal more comfortably than the cutter seen in Fig. 1, which is also intended for the same duty.

One advantage of this class of cutter is the wide range of hole sizes they can cover; a representative set listed has a range from ¼ in. dia. to 6 in. dia.

The advent of the power drill has led to the introduction of many attachments and tools for use in them. Amongst these are modifications of the cutter just described. In tool merchants' catalogues they are sometimes described as 'crown saws', a term that will be self-evident from the way they are constructed. Black & Decker can supply these tools in sizes from ⅝ in. to 2⅝ in. dia.

FORMING HOLES IN SHEET METAL
Large holes in sheet metal are difficult to form clearly if normal drilling methods are adopted. Instead, a press-tool operation is needed if a neat finish is to result. The amateur does not often require to produce such holes, so expensive equipment to do so is scarcely justified if something of a simple nature will do all that is necessary instead, the more so if he can make the tool for himself.

The tool illustrated in Fig. 4 satisfies

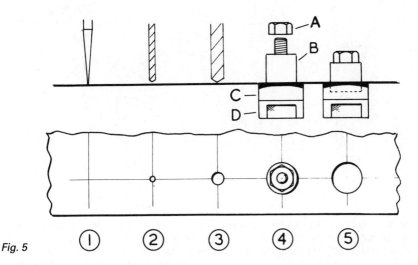

Fig. 5

this requirement: it follows the lines of a commercial product capable of a wide range of work, but it can be made for oneself, with a capability of ⅜ in. to 1 in., from mild steel oddments found in the scrap box.

The device consists of four parts; first the base D, which may be caught in the vice if necessary, or restrained from turning by means of a tommy bar placed in the hole seen in the illustration. Secondly, the bolster C upon which the work is placed. Thirdly, the punch B, which is forced down on the work by the nut A running on the stud that forms part of the base assembly.

The sequence of operations when using the punching device is depicted in Fig. 5 and these are as follows:

(1) Mark off the work and centre punch.
(2) Pilot drill the work.
(3) Open out the pilot-drilled hole so that the work will slip easily over the stud.
(4) Assemble all the parts of the device as depicted in the illustration.

(5) Screw down the nut A till the punch penetrates the work. It is quite easy to assess when the punch has done so because resistance to the nut's turning will vanish immediately the metal has sheared.

Commercially-produced hole cutters of this type are capable of operating on mild steel sheet up to 16 s.w.g. (0.062 in.). The example made by the author, however, being made from mild steel and not hardened, had a limit of about 24 s.w.g. (0.0247 in.).

TREPANNING IN THE LATHE

In order to conserve valuable material it is sometimes advisable to employ a trepanning operation that can be performed in the lathe, a technique depicted in the illustration Fig. 6.

The drawing is based on a simple occurrence in the workshop, when a piece of half-inch light alloy plate was mounted in the 4-jaw independent chuck, in order that a 3-inch disc of material could first be removed before

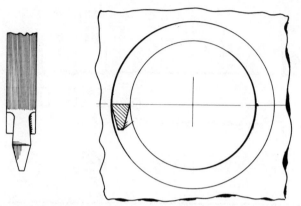

Fig. 6

the plate itself was bored to size. In this way a piece of valuable material was retained instead of being converted into swarf.

As will be seen in Fig. 6 the trepanning is carried out with a parting tool that has its flanks well laid back in order that they will clear the sides of the kerf that the tool will machine as the work proceeds. An automatic feed is a great help here. If the feed itself is independently driven, as is the case in two of the lathes in the author's workshop, then the feed rate can be adjusted for best results.

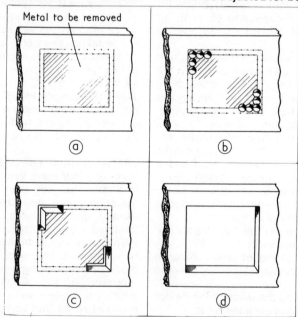

Fig. 7

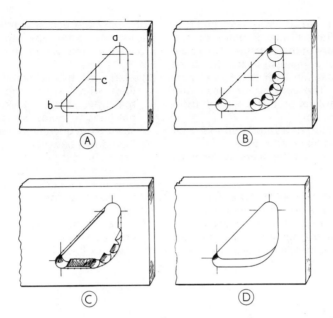

Fig. 8

CUTTING RECTANGULAR HOLES IN PLATE

One is often faced with the problem of cutting holes in plate that are not truly circular so cannot be cut by means of a tool mounted in the drilling machine or in the lathe.

Such holes can either be rectangular or curved and in addition some may be of a type that is open at one end, as are those used as the mountings for the horn blocks for model locomotives. One example of a rectangular hole, together with the four stages needed to produce it, is depicted on the illustration Fig. 7. The procedure is as follows:

(1) As illustrated at (a) mark out the work. Two lines are needed here. The outer delineates the perimeter of the aperture to be cut, the inner is the line upon which a series of centres can be produced for the subsequent drilling operation.

(2) Drill the holes depicted at (b). As will be seen, the size of these holes must ensure that they do not impinge on the perimeter of the aperture.

(3) File away the bridges left between the drilled holes so that a saw can be used to cut down between the worked lines in order to remove the block of unwanted metal seen in diagram (c).

(4) File up to the outer lines to clean the work as depicted at (d).

The series of diagrams Fig. 8 illustrates the sequence of operations involved in cutting a representative irregular aperture. These are as follows:

(1) Mark out the work as seen in the diagram A, using the centres a and b for the drilled holes that form the corners of the work. The centre c is employed for scribing the curved periphery of the aperture.

57

(2) Drill the two corner holes using drill sizes that will just impinge on the periphery of the aperture. The same remarks apply also to the drill used in connection with the curved periphery. The centres for these drill holes are set on a line scribed from the centre c.

(3) Cut out the unwanted material with a saw as depicted at C.

(4) Finally file up the sawn surfaces as seen at D.

CUTTING AN OPEN-ENDED SLOT

Open-ended slots are often encountered in mechanical work, particularly in the making of miniature locomotives. No drilling is needed to produce these slots, only the hacksaw followed by a file to trim up the opening. Therefore, proceed as follows in the illustration Fig. 9.

(1) Mark out the work using double lines within which the saw blade may travel. Mark out also the diagonal lines to guide the blade when sawing out unwanted material (a).

(2) Saw down between the two vertical sets of lines (b).

(3) Remove the right-hand section of unwanted material by sawing along the diagonal line seen in the sketch (c).

(4) Remove the opposite piece of material by sawing along the left-hand diagonal line (d).

Fig. 9

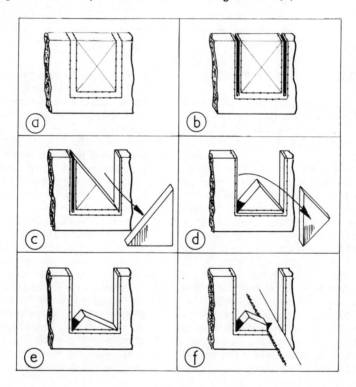

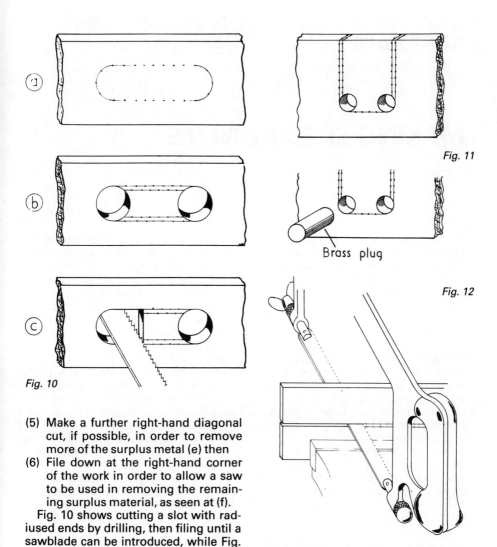

Fig. 11

Brass plug

Fig. 12

Fig. 10

(5) Make a further right-hand diagonal cut, if possible, in order to remove more of the surplus metal (e) then
(6) File down at the right-hand corner of the work in order to allow a saw to be used in removing the remaining surplus material, as seen at (f).

Fig. 10 shows cutting a slot with radiused ends by drilling, then filing until a sawblade can be introduced, while Fig. 11 shows how drilled holes in corners can be protected against teeth marks from sawing by the insertion of brass plugs cut from oddments of suitable rod.

The ability to turn a sawblade 90° in its frame (Fig. 12) should not be overlooked; here the vice jaws offer a guide to help a straight cut while clamping the work firmly.

CHAPTER 8

MAKING SPECIAL NUTS

Some pieces of equipment are improved both technically and artistically by the provision of specially formed nuts holding their components in assembly. Nuts in this category may either be finger-controlled or turned with a spanner, four examples being shown in Fig. 1.

The nuts illustrated at A are used principally on electrical equipment while the barrel nut at B frequently finds employment in the automobile industry where, in locations difficult of access, ordinary nuts would be difficult to tighten. The barrel nut permits spanners to be more readily used.

The nut depicted at C is of rather more than historic interest. It appears to have been developed early in the last century for use in marine steam engines then beginning to be built. Many of these engines embodied a huge degree of ornamentation not now found in modern severely functional engineering design.

The Penn nut, to give it the name by which it is sometimes known, combines both nut and washer so has a definite engineering advantage. The author remembers that the nut was fitted to several editions of the Triumph motor cycle prior to 1914. He had a number of these machines so can testify to the contribution the Penn nut made to the excellent overall finish given to these motor cycles. Unfortunately the Penn nut did not survive the first world war as a general fitment, probably on the score of expense, though some amateurs have made use of it.

The machining of the three forms of nut described can best be outlined by listing the sequence of operations. In the case of the nut shown in Fig 1A

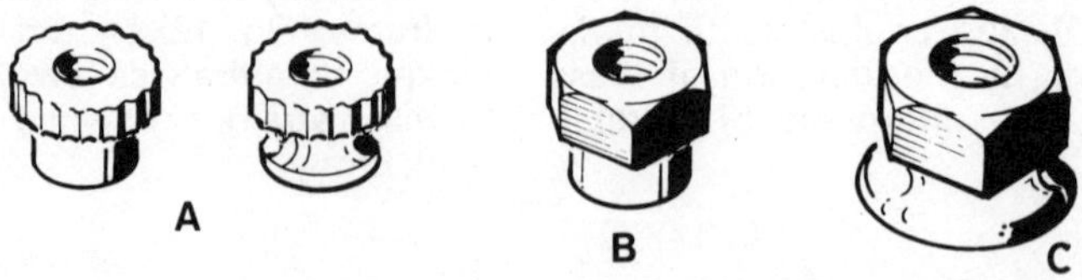

A   B   C

Fig. 1

three tool mountings are needed, a 4-way toolpost on the front of the lathe cross-slide, a 2-way rear toolpost at the back of the cross-slide, and a drill chuck in the tailstock.

The sequence of operations is then as follows:

(1) Turn the major and minor diameters using a knife tool in the front toolpost.
(2) Knurl the major diameter using a knurling tool in the front toolpost.
(3) Centre drill ⎫ All tools set in
(4) Drill tapping size ⎬ tailstock drill
(5) Tap ⎭ chuck.
(6) Chamfer both sides of the knurl pattern
(7) Part off.

A word must be said about the tools used for chamfering and parting-off: these are mounted in the rear toolpost. Both are used inverted and are so depicted in the illustrations Fig. 2 and Fig. 3 where the angular details of these tools are shown.

The chamfering tool, Fig. 2, was designed to cut on either side and it was also intended to be used for facing purposes. To this end the left-hand side of the tool is provided with a radial cutting edge enabling it to operate on surfaces of limited area. The parting-off tool, Fig, 3, has an angled front cutting edge enabling work to be parted off solid bar material without leaving a pip on the finished part. On the other hand a pip is left on the parent material. This, as has been described elsewhere, may be used as an assistance when transferring centres from finished work to a base board mounting, for example.

The Penn Nut The Penn nut is depicted in Fig. 1 at C, while a group of them is illustrated in Fig. 4. The nut on the right of the group is a spare from the author's

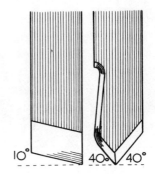

Fig. 2

1914 Triumph motorcycle! If only the Penn nut could be made from hexagon mild steel stock much labour could be saved. Unfortunately it cannot, for the very good reason that the washer component of the nut is greater in diameter than the distance across the flats of the hexagon. One has, therefore, to form the hexagon for oneself by one means or another.

The sequence of machining operations is depicted diagrammatically in Fig. 5. This sequence is as follows:

Diagram A, Fig. 5

(1) Centre drill with drill mounted in the tailstock chuck.

Fig. 3

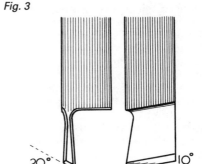

Fig. 4

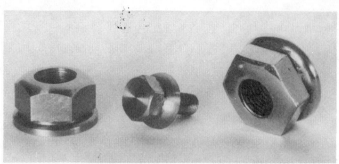

(2) Drill with tapping size drill.
(3) Tap
(4) Turn two diameters, one for the washer component, one to control the dimension over the corners of the hexagon.

Diagram B, Fig. 5, illustrates the forming of the undercut between the hexagon portion of the nut and the washer component. A narrow parting tool is used for the purpose having its front face ground radially in order to produce a rounded finish in the bottom of the undercut.

Diagram C, Fig. 5, demonstrates the use of the hand-graver in order to form the radial or curved edge to the washer component of the Penn nut. The employment of hand tools in the course of turning in metal is a matter of some importance, since the practice can in many instances avoid the necessity for the introduction of specially-made form tools, tools that the non-production workshop would find it uneconomical to provide. It is considered, therefore, that the subject is worthy of independent treatment so this will be covered later.

Diagram D, Fig. 5. Form the hexagon portion, using a filing rest or milling attachment. Some means of using the lathe as a dividing engine has to be provided in order to ensure uniformity in the facets of the hexagon itself. A simple method of doing so is to attach a changewheel to the tail of the lathe mandrel and to engage the wheel with a detent set on some fixed portion of the headstock assembly such as the main casting. The number of teeth in the changewheel must be divisible equally by the number of work divisions featured. For example, if six divisions are needed a 60 tooth wheel can be used and the detent set to engage every tenth tooth. The whole subject of dividing in the lathe is too extensive to be dealt with in the present book, but a simple process such as described is a matter of common sense.

Chamfer both sides of the hexagon using a tool mounted in the rear tool-post, then part off.

Using the Nut Tap When but two or three nuts of any type have to be made the tapping operation, as shown in the diagrams, is best carried out by means of a hand tap set in the tailstock chuck. On the other hand, when a quantity of nuts need tapping it is best to carry out the operation away from the lathe altogether.

The work may be performed in the drilling machine using a simple fixture

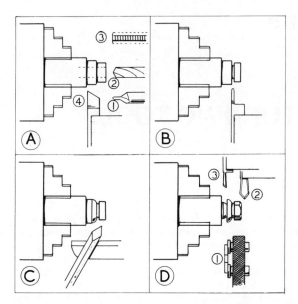

Fig. 5

to hold the nuts and employing a nut tap caught in the drilling machine chuck.

The nut tap differs from the hand tap in that the shank is somewhat smaller in diameter than the core of the threaded portion. This construction allows the tap to pass clear through the nut so that it is possible for a number of nuts to congregate on the shank itself.

As has been said, the operation needs a simple fixture to hold the nuts from turning. The fixture itself is depicted in Fig. 6. It is laid on the table of the drilling machine and clamped in place when centralised under the tap. The fixture is provided with adjustable jaws that allow for any variation in the sizes of the hexagon material used for making the nuts.

The fixture illustrated accommodates nuts from 6BA – 2BA and also a hexagon material size suitable for ³⁄₁₆ in. Whitworth or British Standard Fine thread.

Fig. 6

63

CHAPTER 9

HAND TURNING TOOLS

At one time all turning in the lathe was carried out with hand tools supported on a rest that enabled them to be set at the correct height. If we except thread chasers, only one hand tool for general use now remains in the turner's armoury; this is the graver, illustrated in Fig. 1.

The hand graver was in common use whenever certain operations in the lathe needed to be carried out. For example, if, on a piece of work, a corner needed to be broken or a radial surface had to be machined then the turner would use a graver and finish the work by hand.

It is used by the amateur principally for rounding the corners of turned work and requires both hands to operate it. Assuming the user is right-handed, his left hand grasps the shank of the tool which is supported by the lathe hand-rest while his right hand, taking a firm hold of the handle, controls the movement of the tool itself.

The graver is made from a piece of square section tool steel, ground at 45 deg. to provide a diamond-shaped point and furnished with a wooden handle so that the turner can control the tool correctly. Representative dimensions, taken from various gravers in my

Fig. 1

	A	B	C	DØ	EØ
1	6"	4¾"	5⁄16"	7⁄8"	5⁄8"
2	3½"	4¾"	¼"	DO	DO
3	3½"	3⅛"	3⁄16"	DO	DO

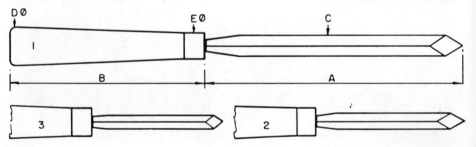

64

workshop, are given in Fig. 1 and in the accompanying schedule.

The graver may be used with its cutting edge set either above the centre of the lathe as for turning steel, or directly upon the centre line when machining brass. The first condition is depicted diagrammatically in Fig. 2. The tool itself is rotated axially while in contact with the work and in rotating its cutting edge forms a curved surface on the corner of the work.

The second condition is illustrated in Fig. 3. Here the cutting edge of the graver is set on the work centre line while the tool as a whole is swung from side to side about the imaginary fulcrum point seen in the diagram.

As may be imagined only light cuts can be taken with a hand tool. Therefore, the speed at which the turning operation is undertaken can be kept high. Should 'chatter' develop, however, the rotational speed of the work must be reduced.

Sharpening the Graver As with any other hand tool the graver must be really sharp to operate successfully. The rough off-hand grinding procedure is best undertaken with the graver blade set in a V-block so that the point of the tool can be presented correctly to the side of the grinding wheel. In order to maintain a consistent 45° angle at the tool point, a simple fence may be clamped to the rest. In this way the graver, which is, of course, itself clamped in the V-block, is correctly presented to the grinding wheel.

The rough-grinding operation usually leaves a wire edge to the cutting surface of the graver. This must be removed by honing the tool on a smooth oil stone in the manner illustrated by Fig. 4.

A TYPICAL HAND-TURNING OPERATION

The amateur is often called upon to produce a ball end on a piece of work that has otherwise been machined by

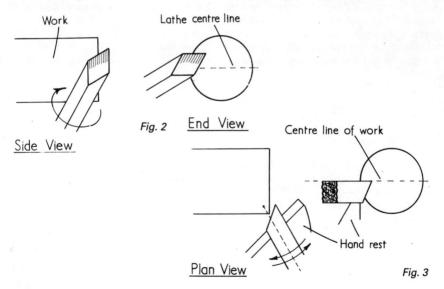

Work

Lathe centre line

Side View

Fig. 2   End View

Centre line of work

Hand rest

Plan View

Fig. 3

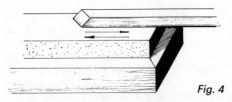

Fig. 4

ordinary turning methods. In this event the hand-graver can solve the problem. It is necessary in the first instance to machine on the end of the component a blank as depicted by the dotted outline in Fig. 5.

The graver can then be applied in the way previously described. The dimensions of the blank are best obtained by setting out the part itself on the drawing board, making the drawing at least twice full size. It will then be a relatively simple matter to measure off the blank directly.

Fig. 6 and Fig. 7 depict the two stages in hand-turning a ball on the end of a parallel shank. The procedure should be self-explanatory, but it should be noted that while a self-centring chuck can be used for the first stage, it is essential that a 4-jaw independent chuck is used for the second stage. In this way it will be able to assure accuracy by setting

the work to run true at the outset. If a tapered shank is needed, this can be machined after the ball is formed by gripping the ball in the self-centring chuck and supporting the end of the shank by the tailstock.

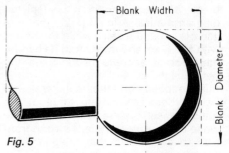

Fig. 5

A TOOL FOR FINISHING BALL ENDS

It will probably be appreciated that a ball end turned by a hand tool is most likely to lack accurate roundness. This state of affairs, however, can be remedied to some extent, with the ball itself being given an acceptable appearance, by making use of the tool illustrated in Fig. 8. The tool itself is made from a piece of silver steel bored to the finished size of the ball to be produced. In use it is swung around the work as

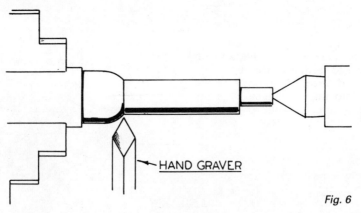

←— HAND GRAVER

Fig. 6

indicated by the arrows seen in the illustration.

As depicted the tool has no top rake to its cutting edge, so is suitable for use on brass. Chamfering the end of the tool some 10–15 degrees would fit it for turning steel.

CATCHING OR STRIKING A CENTRE

There *are* other tools for hand-turning metal but they are more and more museum pieces and the graver remains the only hand-tool likely to be used. Before leaving the subject, there is one use of a graver which may be of service in small shops, that of forming a centre in a piece of work. Modern practice would, of course, employ a centre drill for the job. On the other hand it may well be that no centre drill is to hand, or that centring is needed to start a small diameter drill, so that basic methods must be used to start the work.

The sequence of operations is shown in the series of illustrations comprising Fig. 9. As depicted the first item in the operation is striking a shallow centre (A) into which a drill can be fed. The technique is to have the work turning in the lathe and to place the point of the graver a little way from the apparent centre. With light pressure on the graver, it is moved positively towards the centre and, by 'feel', (there will be resistance to further movement) it will stop its advance; the graver is then pushed into the workpiece by a little extra pressure. Some practice on samples may be advantageous for those unfamiliar with hand held tool techniques (B). This shallow centre is formed by the point of the graver while the drill is fed into the work for a distance that ensures the point of the graver will not bottom in the drilled

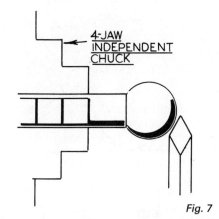

Fig. 7

hole when it is opened out (C) to conical form.

It will be obvious, however, that careful as one may be in hand turning an internal taper the result can never be perfectly accurate. For this reason Holzapffel recommended the use of a 'D' bit to control the cone angle as seen in D(a) the bit being held in the tailstock. Holzapffel also suggests that a pointed tool, supported by the hand rest, can be used with advantage to enlarge the taper before making use of the 'D' bit. Care, however, needs to be taken here to avoid 'chatter'. The tool in question is depicted at (b).

A word about the 'D' bit itself. In case

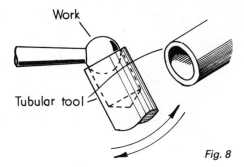

Work

Tubular tool

Fig. 8

67

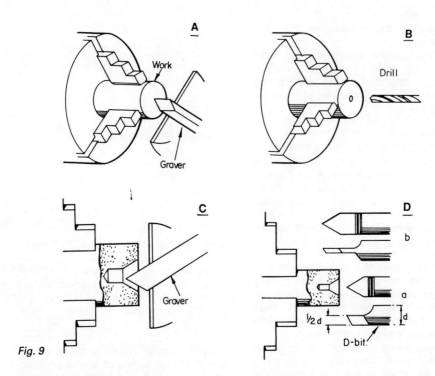

Fig. 9

there are readers who do not know the tool, it is made from round silver steel or high-speed steel having its point, in this case, formed to an included angle of 60 degrees. In order to provide a cutting edge, the body of the bit is filed down to its half-diameter as shown in the illustration. A 'D' bit of this type is only intended for light cuts, a characteristic that makes it particularly suitable for correcting any errors in a hand-formed female centre.

CHAPTER 10

THE WOBBLER

The 'wobbler' is a device enabling work to be set accurately in the lathe. It appears in two forms, the first, a self-contained unit that may be clamped in the toolpost and used without any additional equipment, while the second type is supported by the tailstock and needs the employment of the Dial Test Indicator after being brought into contact with the work.

Both forms are readily made for oneself and constitute a worthwhile exercise in turning and fitting.

The independent type of wobbler is illustrated in Fig. 1 and in section in Fig. 2, where it will be seen to consist of a shank A provided with a spring-loaded cover plate B and a needle-and-ball assembly C located in the shank and retained by the cover plate.

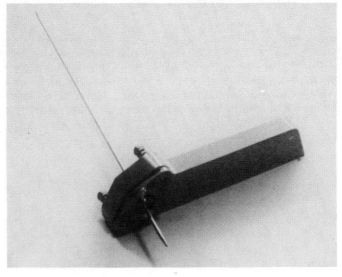

Fig. 1

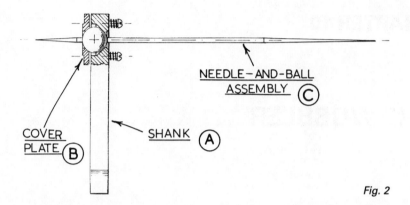

NEEDLE−AND−BALL ASSEMBLY ©

COVER PLATE ®   SHANK Ⓐ

Fig. 2

The device is intended for use in setting work to run accurately either on the faceplate or in the 4-jaw independent chuck. To this end it is clamped with its axis at lathe centre height and the short end of the needle assembly in contact with a centre punched on the work and previously set to run as true as possible by eye. If the lathe is now turned by hand the long end of the needle will describe a circle whose magnitude is determined by the amount of error in the work setting itself. The extent of the needle movement is estimated by bringing up the tailstock with a centre mounted in it in the manner depicted in Fig. 3.

It will be apparent that because of the difference in lengths between the short and long ends of the needle assembly, a small needle movement at the work end will result in a much magnified one at the outer. So that, by adjusting the work until no movement is discernible at the long end of the needle, it is possible to achieve a work setting of some accuracy.

An Alternative Wobbler It will be appreciated that the accuracy of the device just described depends, in the final analysis, on the ability of the human eye to detect small movements of the needle point. However, by making the ratio of the long to the short lengths of the needle high, accuracy of a practical value can be established.

When greater accuracy is needed the

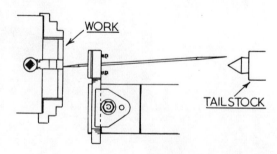

WORK

TAILSTOCK

Fig. 3

piece of equipment depicted in Fig. 4 can be used in conjunction with a dial test indicator. It is believed to have originated from the Union Twist Drill Company of America, who made the example in the writer's possession, and is, in itself, a very simple device consisting of few parts. These are illustrated in Fig. 5 and comprise a body some 6 or 7 inches long drilled and reamed axially to accommodate a plunger centre-drilled at its outer end. A spring is fitted to the tail of the plunger and abuts against the inside of the body.

Figs. 6 and 7 illustrate the way in which this piece of equipment is used. As before, the work is first set to run approximately true by eye. The wobbler is then engaged with its pointed end placed in a centre drilled or punched in the work face. The opposite end of the device is then supported by the tailstock centre, light pressure being applied in order to depress the internal spring and hold the wobbler in place. A dial test indicator is then mounted in the tool-post with an 'elephant's foot' attached

Fig. 4

to its plunger; this is then brought into contact with the body of the wobbler as close to the work as possible. The dial indicator will then read the amount of

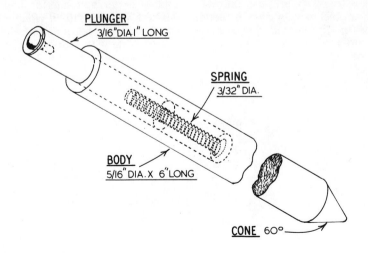

PLUNGER
3/16"DIA.1" LONG

SPRING
3/32" DIA.

BODY
5/16" DIA. X 6" LONG

CONE 60°

Fig. 5

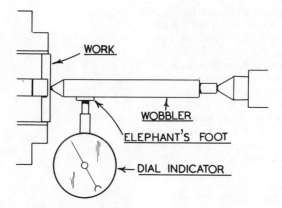

Fig. 6

eccentricity when the lathe is turned by hand, enabling the operator to re-set the work until a nil reading of the indicator is achieved. The work can then be considered as running true to close limits of accuracy.

The making of this particular wobbler should present little difficulty. The body can be made from a length of silver steel drilled and reamed axially to accommodate the plunger which should be an easy sliding fit, but without shake. This part, too, can be made from silver steel, the only work needed on it being the shouldering for the spring and the centre drilling of the outer end.

The 60 degree cone at the nose of the body is best turned to a sharp point and, for preference, hardened and tempered locally to inhibit wear.

MAKING THE SELF-CONTAINED 'WOBBLER'

The Shank A The shank of the device illustrated in Fig. 2 is made from a piece of ⅜ in. mild steel stock marked off in accordance with the detailed drawing Fig. 8. The dimensions given are for a centre finder suitable for use in the Myford ML 10 lathe, in which case the steel stock can be mounted directly on the topslide without packing. It is then set square with the face of the chuck

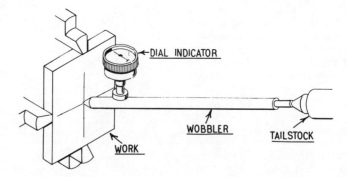

Fig. 7

72

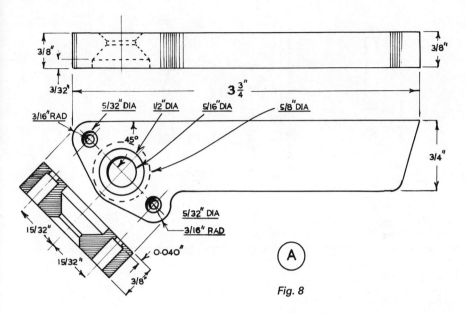

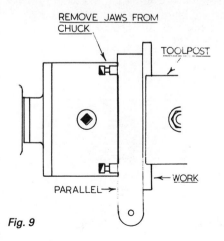

Fig. 8

using a parallel such as a rule for the purpose. The rule is interposed between the face of the chuck and the work and the tool clamp secured as depicted in the diagram Fig. 9, care being taken to see that the work is upright on the topslide; a small square applied to the side of the work will ensure this.

Once the material has been correctly mounted the part can be drilled and the seating for the needle assembly formed with a countersink if one of a suitable size is available. If no large countersink is to hand the shank will need to be machined by normal turning methods with the work bolted to the faceplate and set to run as true as possible by means of a surface gauge. When the seating has been formed the work is reversed on the faceplate, so that the clearance behind the ball seating can be machined.

On the completion of this part of the operation the shank is sawn and filed to shape and the holes for the 6BA screws drilled, leaving the counterbores for the springs until after the cap B has been

Fig. 9

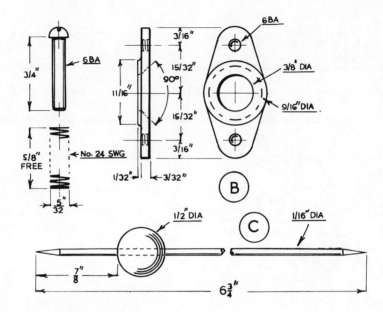

Fig. 10

6BA

3/4"

6BA

3/16"

15/32"
90°

11/16"

15/32"

3/8" DIA

9/16"DIA

5/8"
FREE

No. 24 SWG

3/16"

5/32

1/32"   3/32"

B

1/2" DIA

C

1/16" DIA

7/8

6 3/4"

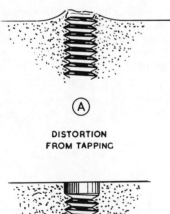

A

DISTORTION
FROM TAPPING

B

PREVENTED BY
COUNTERDRILLING

Fig. 11

made, and drilled and tapped with a ball in place to locate the cap correctly in relation to the shank.

The Cap B (Fig. 10) This part is made from a piece of mild steel material ⅛ in. thick, sawn and filed to shape after machining the countersink for the ball assembly. For this part of the process the work is caught in the 4-jaw independent chuck and reversed to form the 1/32 in. relief on its face. In order to make certain that the spring-loaded 6BA screws that hold the cap in place are correctly drilled and tapped a ½ in. dia. ball is placed in the countersink and the cap is located by this and clamped ready for drilling, packing being interposed between the two parts to ensure that their abutment faces are parallel. The cap is then spot-drilled through the holes in the shank, a No. 34 drill being employed and fed in for a depth that is sufficient to allow the No. 43 tapping size drill to start accurately. When both holes have been drilled clear through, and before they are tapped and while the cap is still in place clamped to the shank, turn the work over and relieve the outside of the holes with a No. 34 clearing size drill for a depth equal to about 1½ threads. After this operation pass the 6BA tap through the shank and thread the holes in the cap, which is now completed so can be detached from the shank.

Referring for the moment to the relieving of the 6BA holes in the cap. The action of a tap in a hole, unless means are taken to prevent it, is to raise the metal round the edge of the hole in the way depicted by Fig. 11 at A. This is a somewhat unsightly effect that not only mars the appearance of the work itself but, when two parts have to abut closely, may stop them from doing so.

It should, perhaps, be added that the counter-drilling operation must be carried out before the hole is tapped. If it is done after, the relief is likely to wander off-centre and spoil the work. The spot drilling of the inner face of the cap already described should be of sufficient depth to ensure that the conditions described are satisfied.

Fig. 12

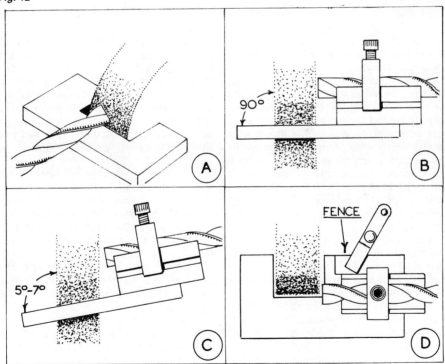

Fig. 13

The spring-seating counterbores in the shank A can now be formed. In the detailed drawing these are given as ⁵⁄₃₂ in. dia. but their size will, of course, depend on what compression springs are available. Ideally the counterbores should be flat bottomed, though this is not essential. However, for those who wish to form them correctly, it may not be out of place to describe a simple method of making counterbores from ordinary twist drills, since, in this way, a wide range of sizes is available and may be used with advantage in other workshop activities.

The making of counterbores from twist drills needs the use of an angular grinding rest which enables grinding on the side of the wheel to be carried out at pre-determined angles.

When making counterbores from twist drills it is suggested that when possible these should be made from old drills so that a range of useful sizes can be built up. The first step is to remove the sharp point of the drill by a rough grinding operation carried out on the face of the wheel, Fig. 12 at A. The drill point is now roughly flattened, so now needs to be ground truly square on the side of the wheel. For this purpose the drill is mounted in a V-block, the angular rest is set square with the wheel and the drill point ground square as depicted in Fig. 12 B.

At this stage the drill will not cut and will not do so unless the cutting lips are 'backed off'. In order to do so the angular rest is set at an angle of some 5–7 degrees (Fig. 12 C) and each lip in turn ground on the side of the wheel. For this purpose again the drill is set up in the V-block with a fence clamped to the angular rest to prevent the grinding extending past the centre line of the drill (Fig. 12 D).

A practical application of the necessary set-up is seen in Fig. 13. The V-block used has a simple bridge clamp to grip the drill and a screw to act as a

Fig. 14

depth stop. A block fixed to the drill shank abuts against this stop and also serves as an indexing device to ensure that each lip is ground evenly. These details are seen in the illustration Fig. 14.

An alternative to the position of the fence shown in the operational sequence Fig. 12 is that shown in Fig. 13. Here the fence makes contact with the front of the V-block which is moved across the side of the wheel. The lip is ground up to the drill centre line, a condition that must be estimated by eye, and the corner of the wheel must be kept sharp or the grinding will not be square. For this reason the wheel should be of fine grit, if possible not less than 80 grit.

But to return to the wobbler itself. All that now remains is to drill the half-inch diameter bronze ball and fit the needle to it. The needle used in the wobbler illustrated is a discarded steel knitting needle approx. 0.070 in. dia. It is secured to the ball by friction only, an undersized drill being used and the needle stoned until the ball is a force fit about one inch from the point.

CHAPTER 11

CASE-HARDENING

Case-hardening, as its name implies, is a process whereby steel parts are given a hard surface layer, leaving the central core as unaltered, soft metal. The effect of the process is depicted diagrammatically in Fig. 1. A typical example is a machine spindle, furnished with a hard skin to resist wear and a core of normal steel to maintain the strength of the part. Other instances are small cutting tools and the service nuts fitted to machine tools where case-hardening resists wear and damage from the continual use of the spanner. The cutting tools require to be finally tempered to remove brittleness from the cutting edges and, although useful for dealing with small batches of parts, they stand up for a surprisingly long time, particularly when machining non-ferrous metals.

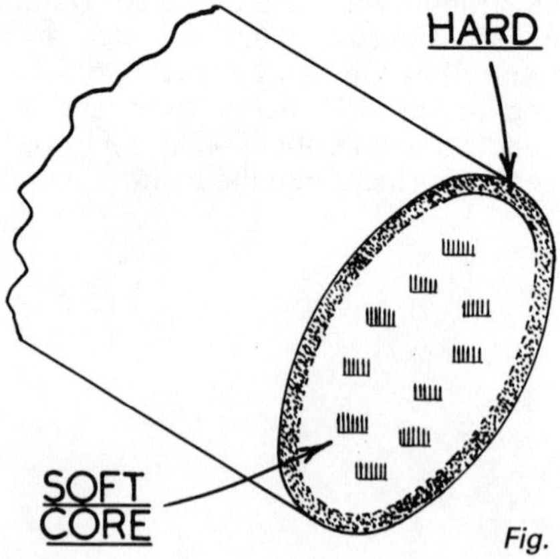

No difficulty has been experienced in case-hardening components made of the ordinary mild steel used in the workshop; although this has a low carbon content, the carbon added during the process is sufficient to convert the outer layer into a carbon steel capable of being hardened when quenched in the heated state.

In commercial practice special steels are usually employed where parts have to be case-hardened in bulk. These steels are of high strength and contain nickel or nickel and chromium. There are various proprietary case-hardening compounds in common use, of which Kasenit and Antol are, perhaps, the best known. Excellent results have been obtained in the workshop with bone dust, free from fat, which is or used to be a by-product of the Birmingham button-making industry. Before use it should be parched by heating on a stove until it resembles ground coffee.

Fig. 1

One advantage of this substance is that it produces an attractive, mottled finish with a fine play of colours.

In addition, bone dust does not cause corrosion or scaling of the steel surface. These characteristics are of importance in the gun-making trade, where the breech parts and lock plates are case-hardened after they have been elaborately hand-engraved, and surface damage is, therefore, inadmissible.

One of the simplest case-hardening operations is that used for protecting fittings, such as service nuts, from damage when in constant use. At the outset, it is advisable to shield the screw threads by plugging the nut with fire clay.

The hardening operation that follows is known as the open-hearth process. The part is placed on a firebrick in the brazing hearth and coated with a thick layer of a fusible compound, such as Kasenit or Antol.

When heated with the blowpipe, the compound melts and forms an adhesive coating that excludes the air. Several further applications of the compound should be made, and the heating continued, before the part is quenched in water. This results in forming an attractive, silvery surface finish on the work.

An alternative method is to melt the case-hardening compound in a cast-iron pot and to soak the part in the molten material, leaving it there for half to one hour. It is then removed and immediately plunged into cold water. In the authors' workshop an old petrol engine casting was used for the purpose. It was provided with a nickel wire loop to enable it to be withdrawn from the furnace when the operation was complete, while the part to be treated was fitted with a wire sling in order to facilitate its removal from the pot and the subsequent plunging into cold water.

The pot was placed inside the furnace and surrounded by pieces of coke in order to heat it evenly. Finally the damper and airslide of the furnace were adjusted in order to ensure steady combustion.

As shown in Fig. 2, the pot was totally enclosed during the soaking process and in this way any fumes produced were taken up the flue and into the open air.

In Fig. 3 the correct method of plunging work into water is shown. From this it will be seen that a vortex is made by stirring the contents of the pail vigorously and then lowering the work into the centre of the vortex itself.

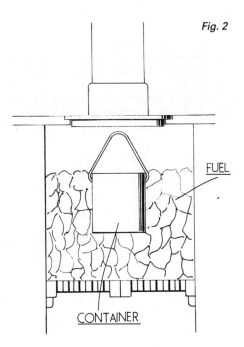

Fig. 2

FUEL

CONTAINER

Fig. 3

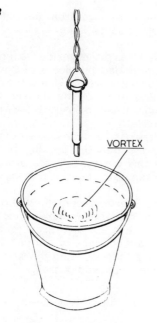

VORTEX

The more usual method of case-hardening is to heat the components in a box firmly packed with the hardening compound.

Cast-iron lidded boxes are best for this purpose, and the electrical switch box, at one time available, Fig. 4, is useful for dealing with small parts. A length of conduit tubing is screwed into the opening provided to serve as a handle, and any other holes should be sealed with metal plugs or fireclay.

The larger components we meet can be housed in an electrical junction box as shown in Fig. 5. Parts for case-hardening should be well cleaned, and the mottled effect obtained with bone dust will show to the best advantage on surfaces that have been highly finished or even polished.

The components for hardening are firmly packed in the bone dust or other compound, so that they are evenly surrounded by a thick layer of the medium. This not only excludes air and ensures direct contact with the parts, but it also gives some support to slender components. If an estimate of the depth of case is required during the heating process, rods of similar material are inserted in holes drilled in the box lid.

These, when withdrawn, quenched and broken across, will show clearly the extent of the hardened layer.

Fig. 4

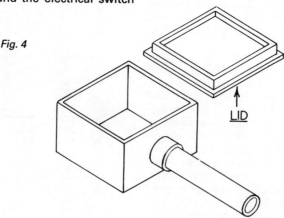

LID

Fig. 5

The simplest way of heating the packed box is in an open domestic fire or stove. The coal or coke should be maintained at an even bright-red heat throughout.

The box is buried in the glowing embers for a period of from one to two hours to obtain a hardened layer several thousandths of an inch in depth. On removal from the fire, the contents of the box are at once tipped into a bucket of clean, cold water, but splashing should be guarded against.

Slender parts are apt to suffer some distortion on heating and quenching.

In keeping with the more advanced methods of heating used commercially, the electrically-heated muffle furnace, illustrated in Fig. 6, was made in the workshop. This has a heating chamber 6½ in. in length, 3 in. wide by 2½ in. in height, made of fused silica under the

Fig. 6

proprietary name Vitreosil.

The consumption of the furnace is approximately 800 watts, and a temperature of 1000 deg.C. can, if required, be reached in 30 minutes.

The central heating chamber is wound with an insulated heating element of nichrome wire and is attached to the outer steel casing, which is furnished with a fire door and mica inspection window. The space between the heating chamber and the outer casing is closely packed with insulating material to prevent heat loss.

An adjustable Simmerstat thermo-switch in the supply circuit controls the temperature of the heating chamber, and enables the case-hardening box to be maintained at a cherry-red heat, termed 'worm-red' by the old-time gun-makers.

The meter can be calibrated, with sufficient accuracy for all ordinary purposes, by using Segar cones. These are made of a fuisible compound which softens and allows the tip to droop when a critical temperature is reached. The series of cones used indicated temperatures of from 600 deg.C. to 1000 deg.C. at intervals of approximately 100 deg.

The following are the temperature changes corresponding to the colours shown by heated steel: dark-red, 700 deg.C.; cherry-red, 790 deg.; bright-cherry, 900 deg.

A cherry-red heat is satisfactory for case-hardening and also for hardening tools made of silver steel when quenched in water or oil. Bone dust is best used in the muffle since, unlike some compounds, it has no corrosive action on the wiring or other metal parts.

In addition to the use of the muffle for hardening and case-hardening, it also provides a convenient means of tempering hardened work.

Small electric muffles are largely used in laboratories, particularly for metallurgical work; they are also employed in various industries for the fusion and heat treatment of metals. These furnaces are manufactured on a commercial scale, but this equipment is necessarily somewhat expensive. It may well be worth investigating the small kilns offered to hobbyists for jewellery enamelling, which will reach the sort of temperatures required without difficulty and which may cost much less than small commercial muffle furnaces. However, the muffles made in the workshop at small cost have given satisfactory service for many years past.

CHAPTER 12

MACHINING SQUARE MATERIAL

The machining of square-section bar material has often to be undertaken in the workshop. In commercial organisations, when quantity production is involved, the equipment available includes collet chucks that permit square-section material to be gripped with great accuracy. In the small commercial and amateur shop the work is usually undertaken using the 4-jaw independent chuck; this involves a somewhat time-consuming operation to set up the work accurately, acceptable perhaps for a single component but scarcely tolerable when numbers are considered.

For accurate work the square material needs to be set truly in the 4-jaw chuck

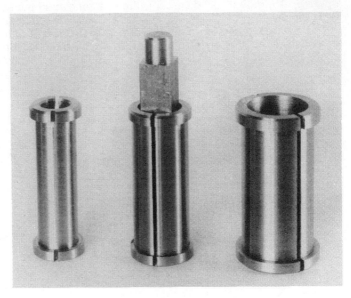

Fig. 1

by means of a dial indicator applied to all four faces of the work in turn. The chuck is then adjusted until the indicator gives an identical reading when applied to each face in turn.

Alternatively, tolerable accuracy can be achieved using the cross-slide index to register the setting of the material in the chuck. The method is simple; the work is first mounted in the chuck and set to run true by eye. Then with a tool secured in the toolpost, the cross-slide feed screw is turned to bring the tool point into contact with the first face of the work. The reading of the index is then taken and noted.

The devices to be described were produced to overcome the difficulty, and to provide a method of holding square-section components accurately enough for most practical purposes. The chuck with which they are used is of the self-centring type; this may be opened and closed quickly enabling the operator to mount or dismount the work rapidly.

The devices depicted in Fig. 1 are essentially liners that are gripped in the chuck jaws and are caused to contract on the four corners of the square material, so gripping it firmly. The three liners seen in the illustration are intended to be used with ¼ in. ⅜ in. and ½ in. square section material respectively.

The illustration Fig. 2 demonstrates the salient sizes needed in making these liners. The dimension C is the same as that of the square material measured across its corners. The dimension B is made about ³⁄₁₆ in. diameter larger than the bore C while the diameters of the collared ends of the liners are again some ³⁄₁₆ in. larger than the diameter C. The liner is slit axially and the collars themselves are relieved diametrically opposite the slit in order to allow sufficient flexing for the liner to grip the work firmly.

The sequence of operations for making the liners is depicted in Fig. 3. The diagrams should be self-explanatory but perhaps a word should be said in extension of the two diagrams C and D. It will be noticed that, in the first of these two diagrams, a register mark has to be punched on the collar opposite the number 1 jaw of the chuck before

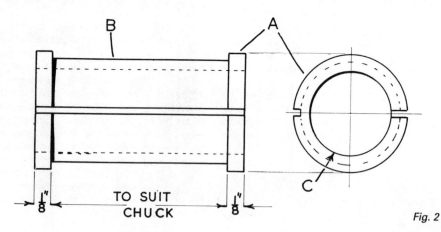

B   A

TO SUIT CHUCK

$\frac{1}{8}''$ $\frac{1}{8}''$

C

Fig. 2

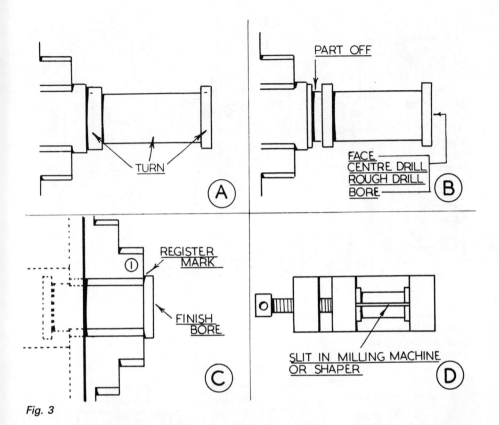

TURN — (A)

PART OFF
FACE
CENTRE DRILL
ROUGH DRILL
BORE — (B)

REGISTER MARK
FINISH BORE — (C)

SLIT IN MILLING MACHINE OR SHAPER — (D)

Fig. 3

the final boring is carried out. This will always enable the liner when removed to be replaced in the chuck jaws with the assurance that work set in it will run truly.

The diagram D shows the liner mounted in the machine vice for the slit to be cut. The diagram indicates that the work can be carried out either by a milling operation or, as performed by the author, by means of a sawing process using a shaping machine.

The process involves the making and use of a special saw frame that can be mounted in the clapper box of the shaping machine, which has means of relieving the cut on the return stroke. Shaping machines, for the most part, have a mechanism that allows the length of their working stroke to be adjusted. When using the saw tool this provision is essential, for the saw itself must be kept within the confines of the work. Otherwise the saw frame will come into contact with the work with disastrous results. If the smaller saw tool is used the same proviso applies, since the short length of saw blade leaving the slit in the work might also prove detrimental.

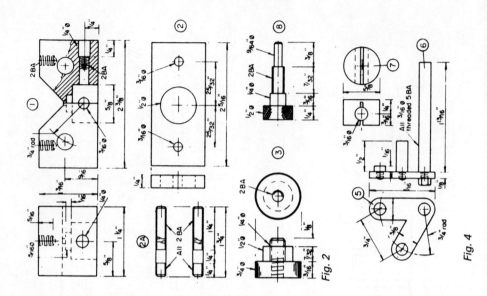

Fig. 2

Fig. 4

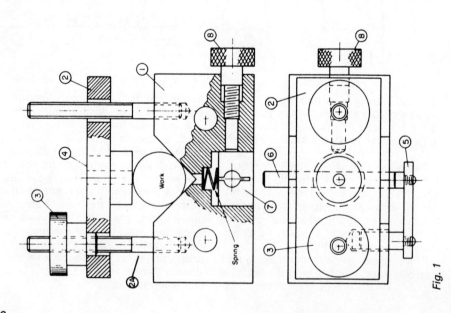

Fig. 1

CHAPTER 13

CROSS-DRILLING JIG

To mark out and set up a one-off job for cross-drilling is a normal workshop procedure, but it becomes tedious if a number of similar items have to be produced; a simple fixture avoiding individual marking and setting is then desirable. That drawn is a jig in use in my workshop, basically very similar to a number made many years ago.

As will be seen the jig is based on a 'V' block, a simple piece of equipment almost essential to any cross-drilling operation. Attached to it by two 2 BA studs (2A) projecting from the block is the work clamp plate (2) held down on the work by two knurled nuts (3). The clamp plate also holds the inter-changeable drill guide bushes (4).

An adjustable work stop is essential and in this case it consists of the following parts: a yoke (5) carrying a pair of stops and an extension rod (6) which is clamped in the base plug (7) in any desired position by the locking screw (8). The yoke carries two stops, one for long work, the other for short. Holes are drilled in the side of the V block to enable either stop to be housed if not directly in use. A spring is fitted above the base plug so that, when the locking screw is slackened, sufficient friction

between the extension rod and the base plug is engendered to ensure that adjusting the work stop is made as easy as possible. An isometric view of the stop mechanism is given in Fig. 3 which should help to clarify the method, while the details of the relevant parts are to be seen in Fig. 4.

If the jig is to function satisfactorily it will be appreciated that the Clamp Plate must be so situated that the drill bushes are centralised in the V of the V block. There are two ways of ensuring this *before* the holes for the two 2 BA studs are drilled and tapped using the clamp plate itself as the drill-and-tap guide. In

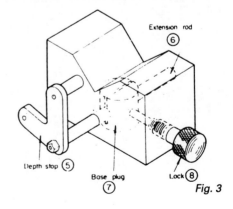

Extension rod ⑥

Depth stop ⑤

Base plug ⑦

Lock ⑧

Fig. 3

87

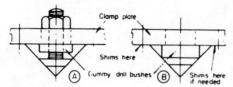

Fig. 5

the first of these methods a dummy drill bush is tapped accurately in the lathe and fitted with a screw having a chamfered head that can be adjusted to make contact with the angular faces of the V block as depicted in Fig. 5 at A. After the screw has been adjusted satisfactorily the clamp plate is temporarily attached to the V block so that the two holes for the 2 BA studs can be drilled and tapped.

Perhaps the simpler of the two methods is that illustrated in Fig. 5 at B. It may also be the most accurate. Here again a chamfered dummy drill bush is employed and brought into contact with the V block. Packing is then introduced under the ends of the clamp plate until the plate itself beds firmly against the top of the V block while, at the same time, the dummy drill bush seats securely in the V.

The V Block

There is really no need to describe in detail all the small parts that make up the Cross-Drilling Jig and the means of machining them. In the case of the V block, however, perhaps a few words may not be out of place. If a shaping machine is available this is clearly the tool for producing the part, and the user will hardly need instruction from me as to its use. If no shaping machine is to hand the work can be machined by fly-cutting in the lathe. In any case the bulk of the unwanted material should first be removed with a hacksaw after having drilled a transverse hole ³⁄₁₆ in. dia. through the block to allow both the saw blade and the cutter to clear when cleaning up the work.

I have suggested fly-cutting in the lathe because, where the tools available in the amateur shop are concerned, it is unlikely that a milling cutter mounted on an arbor and supported by the tailstock could be accommodated. Instead, a fly-cutter mounted in a suitable adaptor and held in the self-centring chuck can normally be brought into play. Fly-cutting is covered in the next chapter.

CHAPTER 14

FLY CUTTING

Fly cutting in principle is carried out with a single-point tool mounted in an adapter that can be caught in either the self-centring chuck or the 4-jaw independent chuck in order to machine work set either on the cross slide or on a vertical slide mounted thereon. It can be applied to surfacing as in the case of the cross-drilling jig previously described as well as the cutting of small gears such as are required by clockmakers.

A fly-cutter of the type suggested is depicted in the dimensioned sketch Fig. 1. It will be noticed that the shank of

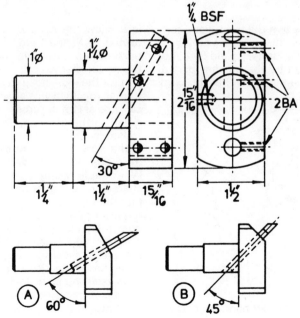

Fig. 1

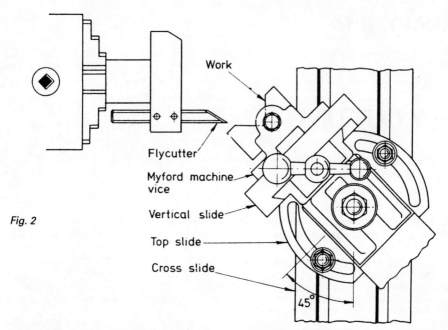

Work

Flycutter

Myford machine vice

Vertical slide

Top slide

Cross slide

45°

Fig. 2

the device has two different diameters. The reason for this is that if only light work is being undertaken the fly-cutter can be gripped by the smaller part of the shank, whereas when heavier work

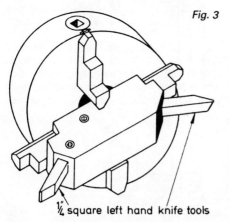

Fig. 3

¼" square left hand knife tools

is in view the smaller end, previously turned to fit the bore of the chuck, is pushed into it, leaving the jaws to grip the major diameter. It is often convenient for the work itself to be mounted in a small machine vice attached to a vertical slide set on the cross slide. The work is fed to the cutter by the saddle controlled by the leadscrew while the travel of the work past the cutter is effected by the feedscrew of the vertical slide itself. When undertaking an operation of this character care must be taken to ensure that the fly-cutter only cuts on the face required, and, in the case of the V block, does not strike its opposite face. This is a matter which can be established by the cross slide feedscrew; once this point has been determined the cross slide itself should be locked.

The set-up for machining a V block is illustrated in Fig. 2 while alternative

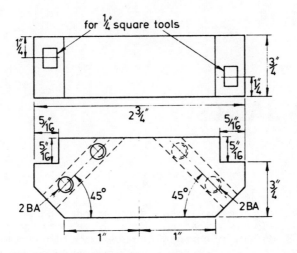

for ¼" square tools

Fig. 4

positions for the tool bit in the fly-cutter itself are depicted in Fig 1 at A and B. This angular positioning of the cutter bit itself depends for the most part on the area of the work it is expected to cover. The fly-cutter illustrated was intended to sweep over a wide area. It therefore has an angular seating for the cutter relative to the cutter block of 30 degrees. With regard to the alternative settings seen at A and B of Fig 1, clearly with the design as it stands it is not possible to make the settings as just a simple matter of adjustment. Instead, the correct angle must be chosen to suit the work in hand after which the seating for the cutter can be drilled and reamed.

As to the cutter itself; this is in effect a left-hand knife tool made from ⅜ in. dia. tool steel and having a flat filed or machined axially along the tool as a seating for the Allen screws which secure the tool in place.

We have said that, in principle, fly-cutting is carried out with a single point tool. By comparison the fly-cutter depicted in Figs. 3 and 4 was designed by the author for mounting in a 4-jaw chuck in order to machine some light alloy components fairly quickly. It consists of a steel block shaped so that the jaws of the chuck can hold it firmly and fenestrated to provide seatings for a pair of ¼ in. tool bits, each secured by a pair of 2 BA Allen screws. The tools themselves are set at 45 deg. to the axis of the block, each again taking the form of a left-hand knife tool with the tips slightly rounded.

CHAPTER 15

SCREW JACKS

Screw jacks in various sizes have long been essential tools in the engineering industry. Even in the small workshop

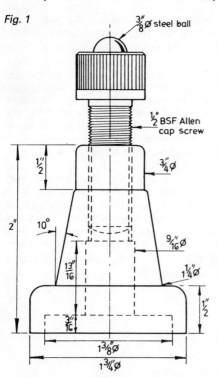

Fig. 1

$\frac{3}{8}''\varnothing$ steel ball

$\frac{1}{2}''$ BSF Allen cap screw

$\frac{3}{4}''\varnothing$

$1\frac{1}{2}''$

$2''$

$10°$

$\frac{13}{16}''$

$\frac{9}{16}''\varnothing$

$1\frac{1}{4}''\varnothing$

$\frac{1}{2}''$

$\frac{3}{16}''$

$1\frac{3}{8}''\varnothing$

$1\frac{3}{4}''\varnothing$

they can well find a place. At one time jacks of a size suitable to the requirements of the small or private workshop were available. For the most part they were products of firms such as Brown & Sharpe and L.S. Starrett in America. Their products were capable of a variety of applications, maybe more than the amateur really needs. I have long since made use of simple jacks, produced many years ago in my shop, in order, to take but one example, to support work overhanging in the vice of the power hacksaw; work that would otherwise tend to be displaced due to the weight of the saw frame and its guiding mechanism, a not inconsiderable force.

These simple jacks are easily made. The base is machined from a short length of mild steel, an odd off-cut from the scrap box will serve, while the screw portion of the jack is simply an Allen cap-screw into the head of which a steel ball of a convenient size has been pressed.

When work has to be milled in the lathe it is sometimes convenient to mount the component on the topslide, catching it, if it is a small one, under the tool

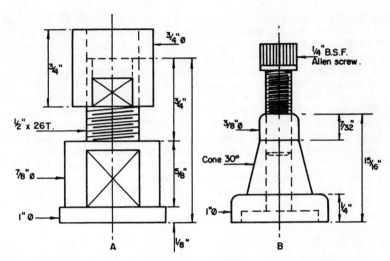

Fig. 2

post clamp. As the tool clamp is already provided with a screw to level the clamp, there is no difficulty in adjusting the whole set-up. But this simplicity is nullified when the usual clamp has to be discarded in order to allow a large component to be set up on the topslide. In such a case a steel strap some ⁵⁄₁₆ in. thick, or more, replaces the tool clamp and is usually adjusted by means of packings to bring it level.

These packings generally have a high nuisance value owing to their propensity for tumbling about at critical moments; but the trouble they cause may be overcome if they are replaced by the sort of jack shown in Fig. 2. As will be seen there are but two parts, a

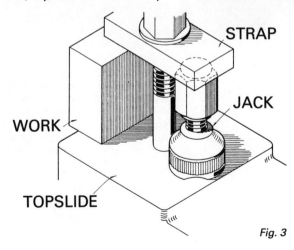

STRAP

JACK

WORK

TOPSLIDE

Fig. 3

base having a threaded pillar machined on it and a barrel nut by which the height of the jack is adjusted.

Convenient sizes for the two parts are: (1) for the base; 1 in, dia. with a ⅜ in. BSF pillar; (2) for the barrel nut; ⅜ in. BSF nut size, ¾ in. long. If necessary the base and its pillar can be made in two parts, in which case the pillar should be made with a collar to register against the base itself in which the pillar is made a press fit. This is preferable to fitting a stud in the base unless the accuracy of the tapping can be guaranteed to ensure that the stud stands vertical.

The jack marked 'A' in Fig. 2 was made in the first instance to assist in the assembly of certain components. But when finished with in this connection it was clear that this jack could be used around machine tools; it was therefore kept. As may be imagined from its construction, the jack was made out of pieces from the scrap box.

The jack marked 'B' is one of a series made in different sizes for use on the marking-off table. This is the smallest of the series.

Fig. 3 shows the methods of workholding on the topslide discussed above.

INDEX

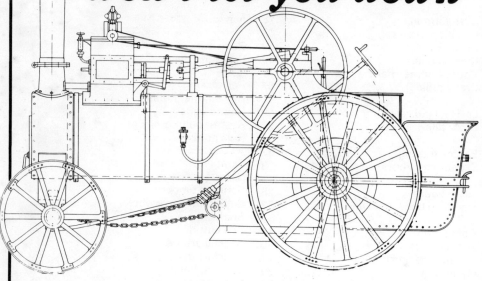